Praise for "*This*

"**I dare you to read this book.**

The United States is the only country in the western world where medical professionals aggressively promote the removal of the most sensitive part of the penis. Be prepared to be shocked by Georganne Chapin's memoir as she unveils the irrational beliefs and corrupt motives underlying the national tragedy of "routine" circumcision. If you are a circumcised male, you are going to be upset. If you are the partner of a circumcised male, you will realize that the sexual problems between you may not be his fault. And if it's not too late, you will protect your son.

Circumcision is an issue whose time has come. What are you going to do about it? Who will you tell? Whose side are you on?

I dare you to read this book."

—**Dean Edell, MD,** American physician and broadcaster

"Alternately touching, frightening, informative and fierce, *This Penis Business* is a powerful narrative of personal drive and a global call for awareness and justice. With the precision of a surgeon, the author has laid open the pages of her life and the steps in her journey toward exposing the dangers of circumcision. I was brought to my senses, and to my knees, more than once in the reading of this brilliant memoir."

—**Julie Evans,** author of *Joy Road: My Journey from Addiction to Recovery*

"When I was a new journalist, Georganne Chapin opened my eyes to a shocking truth: Many medical procedures have no clinical evidence to support them, especially infant male circumcision. *This Penis Business* charts her path to becoming the nation's leading voice in ending this unnecessary and often harmful practice."

—**Joy Victory**, writer and health journalist

"I have known Georganne Chapin for over 50 years as a friend, occasional colleague, and always a fierce advocate for health care justice. This engaging, witty memoir has shown me how much I had missed. Thanks for bringing me up to speed."

—**Henry Ehrlich**, author of *A Time to Search: The Moving and Dramatic Stories of Adoptees in Search of Their Natural Parents*

"With this book, Georganne Chapin is doing the heavy lifting of helping parents make informed decisions around an almost exclusively cosmetic, yet shockingly normalized surgery."

—**Nathan Riley, MD**, The Holistic OB/GYN

"Like the cries of the circumcised boys she's dedicated much of her life to advocating for, Chapin's story cries out to be heard. Inspiring, and at times confronting, this book is a must-read for anyone working to advance children's rights."

—**Jonathan Meddings**, Chair, Darbon Institute, Berwick, Victoria, Australia, and author of *The Final Cut: The Truth about Circumcision*

"*This Penis Business* recounts the making of a heroic children's rights activist while exposing the elephant in the room: the ongoing, prevalent, and profound abuse of infant boys for profit. Georganne Chapin is not afraid to call out the medical industrial complex for its harmful and fraudulent practices that sacrifice the health and wholeness of our sons.

This book will lift us out of collective blindness and denial—and into advocacy and protection for the most vulnerable among us: children. If you care about the psychological, physical, and sexual health of our boys and men, you must not look away."

—**Ruthie Fraser,** somatic trauma practitioner, movement educator, and author of *Stack Your Bones: 100 Simple Lessons for Realigning Your Body and Moving with Ease*

"I have been a longtime supporter of Georganne's mission and organization, Intact America. I both commend and am so grateful to Georganne for having taken up the mantle of wise woman and used her power and wisdom to protect, defend and advocate for boys in our society to remain fully intact from birth, so they can enjoy physical wholeness and full sensitivity. Our children will go through enough trauma in their lives without unnecessary physical mutilation from birth. There should no place for circumcision and the life-long irreversible damage, pain and recognized, or unrecognized latent physical, sexual or emotional trauma it can bring. Read this book and join the movement to stop genital mutilation of our men and enable the re-sensitization and blossoming of society."

—**Professor Elizabeth J. Kucinich**

"Georganne Chapin's deep dive into this most delicate and important subject is sure to enlighten those new to the issue. Those already familiar with it will get a fascinating look into how circumcision impacted Georganne's life."

—**John W. Travis, MD, MPH**, author of *Wellness Workbook*

"This Penis Business is a compellingly honest, kind, sometimes raw account of Georganne Chapin's journey from a dislocated childhood to her current leading role challenging the widespread, damaging US practice of 'routine' infant penile circumcision. Georganne's integrity and compassion for everyone affected is a beacon of light in the dark underbelly of a ubiquitous money-making practice performed despite the medical evidence, and not because of it."

—**Antony Lempert, MD**, lead medical advisor to the (UK) National Secular Society

"Cocksure, fiercely intelligent, and driven by her ideals, Chapin makes clear why she was given the reins to lead Intact America."

—**Lisa Braver Moss and Rebecca Wald**, co-authors of *Celebrating Brit Shalom*

THIS PENIS BUSINESS

A Memoir

GEORGANNE CHAPIN

with Echo Montgomery Garrett

LU☾ID
HOUSE
PUBLISHING

LU☾ID
HOUSE
PUBLISHING

Published in Marietta, Georgia, United States of America by Lucid House Publishing, LLC
www.LucidHousePublishing.com.
©2024 by Georganne Chapin
All rights reserved. First Edition.
This title is available in print and e-book format.
Cover design: Troy King
Cover photo: Echo Montgomery Garrett
Author photos: Kevin Garrett
Interior layout: The Design Lab Atlanta, Inc.

This memoir is based on the author's memories along with her many years and experiences as a prominent leader of the movement to protect every child's right to normal, intact genitals. She has devoted the past two decades of her life to this cause and has written and spoken widely on the topic. This book also contains portions of emails and communications from different people, whose lives and relationships have been damaged by the practice of male genital cutting. Several names have been changed for the sake of privacy.

Library of Congress Cataloging-in-Publication Data:
Chapin, Georganne, 1951-
Garrett, Echo Montgomery, 1960-
This penis business: a memoir/ by Georganne Chapin and Echo Montgomery Garrett–1st ed.
Library of Congress Control Number: 2023950535
Print ISBN: 9781950495450
E-book ISBN: 9781950495467
1.Activist Memoir 2. Family dysfunction 3. Civil Rights 4. Circumcision injuries and deaths
5. Circumcision complications 6. Genital mutilation 7. Foreskin amputation 8. Human rights
9. Infant trauma 10. Long-term grief 11. Post-traumatic stress 12. Sexual dysfunction
13. Medical ethics 14. Iatrogenic injuries 15. Greek-American/Hawaii 16. Forcible foreskin
retraction 17. Adverse childhood experiences 18. Men's rights
BIO032000, BIO019000, MED058090, FAM038000

Lucid House Publishing books are available for special promotions and bulk purchase discounts.
For details, contact info@LucidHousePublishing.com

Chip, age 21, and Ernesto, age 2½

For my brother Chip Chapin,
whose wounding shortly after birth
provoked my eventual awakening to the
terrible truths about circumcision.

⁓

For my son Ernesto Echeverria, who thanked me for sparing him,
introducing me to a world of knowledge I'd never imagined.

⁓

For my friend Lucie Wood Saunders,
who asked how I got into "this penis business."

⁓

For every person who has been damaged by the mindless
and promiscuous practice of genital cutting.

⁓

For my close friends and family who have
encouraged me to write this book.

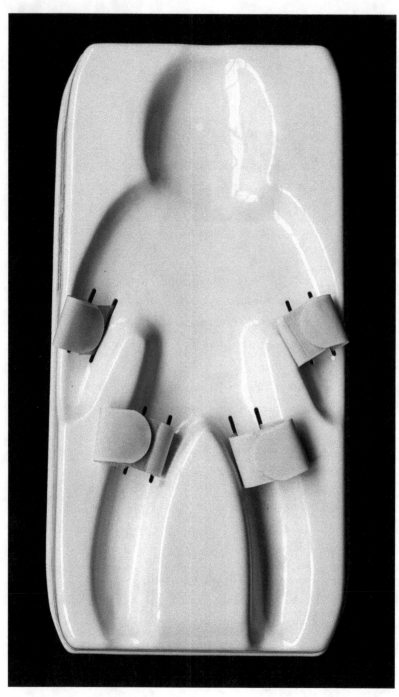

Circumstraint used to immobilize the baby

Contents

**Part Three: Balancing Act: Administration, Idealism, Advocacy...
and a Personal Life**

Part Four: Becoming An Intactivist

Part Five: Action and Accountability

An activist is someone who cannot help but fight for something.

That person is not usually motivated by a need for power or money

or fame, but in fact is driven slightly mad by some injustice, some

cruelty, some unfairness so much so that he or she is compelled

by some internal moral engine to act to make it better.

—EVE ENSLER

My theory is that there is less indelicacy in speaking out your highest,

deepest, tenderest emotions to the world at large, than to almost

any individual. You may be mistaken in the individual; but you

cannot be mistaken in thinking that, somewhere among your fellow-

creatures, there is a heart that will receive yours into itself.

—NATHANIEL HAWTHORNE

First, do no harm.

—HIPPOCRATIC OATH

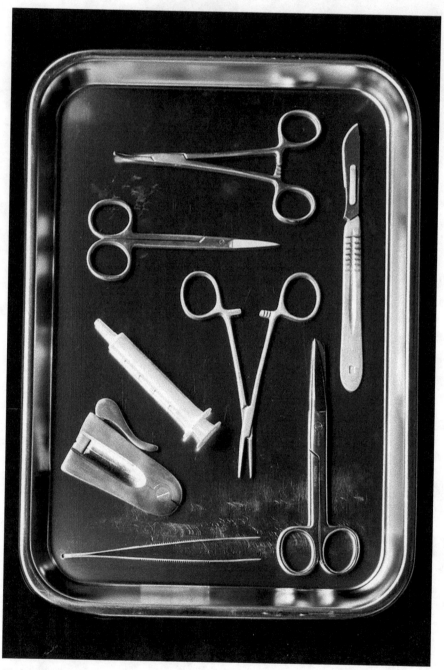

Tools of the trade

PREFACE

Over the past two decades, more people than I can count have asked me how I became involved in fighting against infant circumcision. How did I come to understand that the routine amputation of American baby boys' foreskins has lifelong consequences for everyone in that baby's orbit? The answer is that I paid attention. I listened, and I learned.

In the beginning, my response required little thought because the answer seemed obvious. "Well, it just makes no sense to cut off part of a newborn baby's body." Or I'd ask rhetorically, "Why is it okay to cut a boy's genitals, but wrong to cut a girl's genitals?"

As time went on and I heard from more and more men of all ages who despaired their loss of foreskin, from mothers wracked with guilt because they'd signed off on circumcision surgery and saw their babies return from "the procedure" spent and traumatized, and from fathers who said variations of "I thought my son should look like me, and my son suffered." Story after story alerted me to an undercurrent of sadness and regret in men who had been circumcised.

Like so many other injustices, circumcision has a complicated history. Beginning with the Victorian era in the mid 1800s, circumcision was used as a social control on men and boys, whose sexual appetites were perceived as immoral and even dangerous.[1] Circumcising baby boys came

1

in vogue among the wealthy elites in the 1920s when childbirth became the province of a new surgical specialty: obstetrics and gynecology.

This scientifically spurious medical practice became embedded in American medicine by the 1940s in the wake of World War II, when the military pushed it as a matter of cleanliness and conformity. By the 1950s, 90 percent of all women in the United States gave birth in hospitals, and foreskin amputation was becoming "routine," billed as a "fee-for-service" procedure in a privately funded medical care system. In contrast, other English-speaking countries such as the United Kingdom, New Zealand, and Australia, while sharing the Victorian history of medicalized circumcision, began to give up the practice as they established government-funded medical care and declined to pay for "treatments" that had no utility. In Canada, the frequency of male circumcision today varies by geography and policy of the various provinces; it will likely stop there when circumcision ends in their neighbor to the south. Today in the United States, the medical industrial machine peddles circumcision from the moment the sex of the unborn child is known.

As I learned more, I asked myself and others: *How can it be ethical for a doctor to cut a healthy, normal body part off a person who has no say in the matter?* I also began to wonder: *How deep does this problem go?*

This book is an attempt to explore and explain the answer to these questions, and respond to my anthropologist friend Lucie Saunders' musing, delivered in her intentionally preserved Virginia accent with a fluttering of her hands: "How did you get into this...this *penis* business?"

To answer these questions, I have called upon seven decades of my own memories and experiences and have considered those of family members born before and after me. I was compelled to examine how my somewhat unorthodox upbringing and uncommon world views, my professional pursuits, my personal losses, and my compassion for the losses of others, along with my anger against injustice, all came together to make me a leader in the most compelling human rights frontier of the 21ˢᵗ century. I can think of nothing more important than protecting children from harmful and medically unnecessary surgeries on their sex organs, carried out without their consent to satisfy the demands of culture, profit, parental preference, or religion.

Perhaps the most essential question I have been asked, and the question I was driven to explore as I was writing this book, is *Why do you care?*

I care because male circumcision is a painful and gratuitous injury inflicted on baby boys. I believe that the trauma and damage it causes is at the root of much misunderstanding and painful conflicts within family constellations—between parents and sons and between intimate partners over their lifetimes. I want to convey the profound emotional, sexual, and cultural consequences of routinely and casually mutilating male genitalia in medical settings throughout the United States. And I want infant and child circumcision to end.

I look forward to a time when hospitals stop selling the surgical practice of foreskin amputation as a healthy choice—because there is no evidence to uphold that claim; when doctors simply say, "I don't do that procedure" because they no longer want to mindlessly hurt babies; and when nurses join together and announce, "We are not going to be accomplices in this assault on newborn boys."

I await the day, long overdue, when American insurance companies and the U.S. government stop paying for the "benefit" of circumcision—which has already happened in other westernized countries that corrected their course based on scientific evidence that circumcision is extremely invasive, confers no benefit to boys' health, and imposes considerable risk and unjustifiable costs upon children and their families.

My hope is that you will come away from this book willing to think about, first, how "this penis business" may have impacted your own life and, second, what you can do to ensure that future generations are protected from its wide-ranging harmful effects, including catastrophic injuries and even death. My hope is also that you will use what you learn here—as well as your own common sense, natural empathy, and compassion—to begin speaking out about something most people don't want to hear or acknowledge.

Change begins with connection, communication, and understanding the context of an issue. It continues as a result of conscience and a commitment to action. I could not have predicted that my upbringing, education, and professional experience would lead to my co-founding and becoming the leader of Intact America, an organization dedicated to ending male child genital cutting and upholding human rights. Yet my course to being involved in this penis business was steady and enduring.

Please join me in carrying the message that all children deserve the right to grow up with their bodies and genitals intact, and that the intact male penis with its protective foreskin is a healthy and natural part of the male anatomy. Anyone who denies these truths has an agenda based on neither science, common sense, nor concern for the wellbeing of boys and men and the people who love them.

Prologue

REVELATION

It was September 1998. My son Ernesto and I were spending Labor Day weekend at a farm in Vermont with my half-brother Paul and his wife Katherine's family. Paul's in-laws, Fred and Judy Buechner, were hosting a big gathering for my niece and goddaughter Caroline's christening.

I was hanging out in the kitchen with the women. On a cheese-and-cracker delivery mission, I walked into a raucous conversation among the men in the living room. There was Ernesto, standing and punching his fists into the air, shouting, "You guys just don't know what you're MISSING!"

From the crowd: good-natured jeers.

From Ernesto: "You're like the dude who bought one of those new Cadillacs and can't admit he got a lemon!"

More laughter.

Then, "Except that guy can always fix it or buy another one, but you can't do that. You can't get a new one."

I knew what he was talking about. We'd had a conversation or two about circumcision over the years. Ernesto had mentioned to me that his close friend Willi was the only other kid he knew who wasn't cut. And once, when he was age eleven, and I heard him exclaim from the shower: "Oh my god! This is amazing!"

"What's going on?" I asked through the closed bathroom door.

"You've got to see this, Mom!"

I opened the door, and he was standing there naked and soaking wet. "This is amazing!" he repeated. "I never knew it could slide back and forth."

Now, we didn't go naked in our household, and I had not looked at my son's genitals since changing and bathing him when he was a baby and a toddler. But, having an intact (uncircumcised) husband, I certainly knew what he was talking about. I also could see how genuinely impressed he was with the discovery of the power of a mature foreskin. I backed out and closed the bathroom door.

In the six years between that incident and the Vermont weekend when he pontificated to a roomful of men, I do not remember having a single conversation with Ernesto about his (or anyone else's) genitals, let alone his pubescent revelation.

But now, the penis once again was a topic of conversation. We headed out Monday morning, Ernesto driving my silver Passat west on Route 315 between Rupert, Vermont, and the New York State line. I asked about the commotion from the day before: "What was all that about?"

"Oh," he answered, an incredulous look on his face. "Those dudes were trying to tell me that *not* circumcising is a fad. That just makes no sense. How can it be a fad to leave your body the way it was made?"

"Mom," he continued, glancing toward me in the passenger seat. "I never thanked you and Dad for not having me circumcised. Thank you so much!" He drew out the last two words.

That moment is burned into my psyche. We were cresting a hill and it was a sunny, perfect early fall day. Had I been driving, I would have needed to pull off the road to catch my breath.

Here was my boy, now a young man, fully aware of the exquisite pleasure conferred by a complete penis, and utterly cognizant that men without foreskins were—literally and figuratively—missing something really
important. And he was grateful to his parents for sparing him that fate.

As crazy as it seems to me now, until that moment saying "no" to
circumcising a baby boy was mainly about common sense. How could it
be necessary or important to remove a normal, natural body part from
a young child? How could it be that half of the population (males) are
born requiring surgical correction? And why on earth would we subject a
newborn child to pain when there is no medical need for the surgery in
question? Thankfully, my son's father—born in Argentina and intact—
felt the same way I did when our son was born. No discussion, no argument. Just, "Of course, we're not going to cut off part of his penis."

But despite my own personal experiences and observations; despite
my revulsion at female genital cutting (FGC) and knowing that the
damage inflicted was lifelong; despite my loud protests about American
hypocrisy in condemning FGC while endorsing male genital cutting—
despite ALL of this, I'd never stopped to think about the long-term implications of amputating a boy's foreskin. I had not devoted much thought
to the deprivation of sexual sensation, the alteration of sexual function,
and psychological damage ensuing from this primal wound.

Those revelations, those lessons, would come later. But the day my
son said, "thank you," was really the first day I became an **intactivist**
(one who campaigns against involuntary, nontherapeutic routine infant
or child male genital cutting, commonly called circumcision), a term I
had not heard before.

PART ONE: ROOTS

Chapter One

LONESTAR

W here are you from? The answer to this question varies, depending on who is doing the asking and what they really want to know. The short answer is Texas. Given what most people know about me, it always elicits surprise. No cowboy boots. No Texas accent. No puffy hair. I do love Willie Nelson, though.

My mom, Helen Geracimos, a Greek from Hawaii, met my father, Joseph Arthaud, an Oklahoman of Scottish, German and French ancestry, when she and my grandmother were vacationing in California shortly after the end of World War II. Each of my parents was intrigued by the other—my father titillated by my mom's Hawaii roots and my mom impressed with my father's ambitions. He'd graduated from one of the California state universities and told her his plan was to work as an international journalist.

My mom had completed two years of college at the University of Hawaii, where she'd been crowned Miss Caucasian UH (even in the 1940s, the school was acknowledging different standards of beauty among its ethnically diverse student body). She left college to marry my father, and they moved to Helotes, a tiny town in the Texas Hill Country.

My mom stayed home, and my father worked, but I have no idea what he did there.

On December 2, 1951, I was born in a twelve-bed hospital in nearby Boerne (pronounced Bernie). Both Helotes and Boerne are now northern suburbs of San Antonio, but in the early 1950s, they were rural. My black-and-white baby photos show me in the arms of my stylishly dressed mom, who was age 25 at the time of my birth. I don't have any photos of me with my birth father. My mother threw them all away.

She almost never talked about her marriage to my father. I do know they didn't last long in Helotes. When I was not yet two years old, she left my father and took me back to Honolulu.

One of my treasured family photos shows my mother and me, bedecked in flower lei, departing just a few months after our arrival in Honolulu. This is the only image I have of my blond, handsome Greek grandfather George. We flew back to Texas, this time to a new home in the city of Midland. My mother later told me her own father talked her into returning to Texas to my father. She believed it was because my grandfather feared he wouldn't be able to support us. Sadly, that brief return to Hawaii was the last time my mom saw her father. He died suddenly of a heart attack a few months after our departure.

My father had entered the oil business in the same town George W. Bush called home. Upon our arrival, my mother knew that her absence had done nothing to improve her marriage. My father drank, spent money irresponsibly, and was generally unreliable. But she became pregnant with my sister Julia almost right away. Then in 1955, when Julia was only a few months old, my mother contracted polio during what would be the last epidemic of the often deadly virus in the United States. I remember her lying on the sofa with a "terrible headache." Shortly thereafter she was admitted to the hospital.

When my mother was fighting for her life in an iron lung, my father began to travel—supposedly for business. Our next-door neighbors, a Christian Scientist family named McConnell, stepped in to take care of Julia and me while my mother lay in the hospital wondering if she would live, let alone walk again. Years later she told me that as she pondered her future, she promised herself that, should she survive, she would leave my father. Remarkably, she made a nearly complete recovery.

I remember a year or two later in Honolulu, visiting a college friend of hers who'd also contracted polio. Jeanette was far less fortunate than my mother. I watched her roll around her kitchen in a wheelchair, showing us how she could prepare food and do dishes because of the low countertops her husband had installed. Even at my young age, I understood how lucky my mother—and all of us—had been. Because of her illness, our family was among the first wave of Americans to receive the Salk polio vaccine.

Despite my father's reprehensible behavior and my mom's bitterness toward him, my own memories of him are neither negative nor traumatic. When he was around, he was warm and funny and entertaining— the same qualities that made him the life of the party among people who didn't know (or didn't mind) that he was neglecting his family. I remember how he'd pick me up and hug me when he came in the front door after work. I remember his Midwest twang—calling the men "buddy" and the women "darlin'"—and his love of animals. We had a black Scottish terrier whom he adored but which had to be given away because he bit people.

As soon as my mom was well enough to travel, she took Julia and me to Santa Fe, New Mexico, to get away from Midland and my father, renting a house belonging to the American anthropologist and author Oliver Lafarge for a few months. Living in the home of Oliver LaFarge, author of the 1930 Pulitzer prize-winning novel *Laughing Boy*, about a young Navajo boy, must have helped my mother's motivation. I remember the old house, built in the thick-walled adobe style and filled with books and Native American art, was conveniently near the town square.

The next move, after the briefest stop in Texas, turned out to be a return once again to Honolulu. That was home. Honolulu was where we had a house to live in and my grandmother (whom we called by the Hawaiian word *Tutu*) to help care for us. But before boarding a plane for Honolulu, we spent a couple of weeks with our Greek relatives in the Sunset district of San Francisco. Tutu's siblings had emigrated in two waves from the area surrounding Sparta in the Peloponnese in the earliest years of the 20th century. Her father arrived in 1900 with his sons, followed six years later by her mother with the girls. All of them but Tutu remained in the Bay area. She moved to Hawaii in the early 1920s, after meeting my grandfather—also from Sparta.

While several of my grandmother's siblings never had children, my Aunt Helen married an Italian grocer and gave birth to five sons, my mother's first cousins. They, in turn, had twelve children among them, mostly clustered around the ages of my sister and me. Though these were technically my second cousins, no such distinction was made. We were all family.

Once we returned to Honolulu, then later moved on to New Mexico followed by Ohio, for all practical purposes the San Francisco relatives were as far from me as my immigrant grandparents had been from their own families in rural Greece. Lack of money to travel was one factor. Another, perhaps, was my mother's education and left-leaning politics, which set her apart from her conservative working-class family.

Yet, this brief stay in San Francisco in 1956 gave me a sense of warmth and familiarity. It was enough to make me wish for more connection, as well as to give me an incipient, vague awareness of my isolation. After eight years in Texas, my mom was reaffirming her Greek immigrant roots as she headed home to the Hawaiian Islands. Her multiple identities as Greek, as American, and as a local *haole* in her beloved Hawaii would underlie her academic and philosophical interests over the next four decades.

Not surprisingly, over my lifetime I too have borne conflicted feelings around identity, compounded by a deep sense of loss, and a wistfulness for a stronger connection to my roots.

Chapter Two

ALOHA, AGAIN, TO MY GREEK FAMILY

T he first penis I saw belonged to my cousin Steven. I was five years old, and it was soon after we returned to Honolulu from Texas for a second time to live with my grandmother.

Tutu lived in a two-story house my Greek immigrant grandfather had bought around 1940 for my mother, my aunt, and my grandmother. He had lived there, too, until his death in 1954, even though he and Tutu were divorced. The house was in Makiki Heights—a luxury location now, but a middle-class Honolulu neighborhood at the time. We arrived in "the Islands" in early summer of 1957—long before jet travel and the building boom that took over Oahu in the 1970s and subsequently transformed the state.

From most of the Makiki Heights house—set high up on a hill, with huge windows and sliding glass doors—you could see Diamond Head and the Pacific Ocean only a couple of miles away. Honolulu wasn't hot in those days. Paradise was yet to be paved over with parking lots and freeways. The famous trade winds meant there was always a breeze, and the nights were chilly. Our house, with its single-panel, unpainted cypress wood walls even had a fireplace, though I never saw anyone build a fire in it.

As my mom had vowed before leaving Texas, she returned to the University of Hawaii to finish her bachelor's degree, and also earn a master's in English. The three years I spent in Honolulu with my grandmother, mom, and sister Julia were a happy and secure time in my life.

The house was divided informally into three units. The upstairs (the main floor accessible from the back street) was rented to a friendly *haole* couple named Muriel and Fred. Tutu, my mom, Julia, and I—and an orange cat named Tommy—occupied the two units on the lower floor, separated only by a door that was always kept open. Sliding glass doors opened onto the only flat part of the property, a yard planted with spongy Japanese lawn grass and pink and yellow plumeria trees. The rest of the property was a steep slope, navigable by several flights of steps between the lower road and the upper road.

All the homes on our side of the street had two addresses. Our official address was 2052 Mott-Smith Drive, but you could only get to the house from the narrow upper road in back, which was called Kalawahine Place. That's where we had the carports and the mailbox, with twenty or so narrow steps down and another eight or ten up to reach the upper level, or twenty more down to the lower level. To reach the house from the lower road, Mott-Smith Drive, entailed climbing a good 80 lava rock steps, something we seldom did.

On the other side of Kalawahine Place was Hawaiian homestead land, where native families had lived for decades with only quasi-title to their properties. Often, some of the Hawaiian girls would come into our yard to pick lychees or avocados, and we'd sit together in the lychee tree listening and singing along to popular music on their transistor radio.

We also sang traditional Hawaiian songs that I'd heard my mom play on her ukulele when we still lived in Texas. My love of popular, folk, and traditional music, and my ability to remember melodies and lyrics, go back a long time.

On weekends and during vacations, one or more of my cousins from Lanikai, on the other side of the island and reachable only by the narrow and treacherous Old Pali Highway, would come to visit. (The current Pali Highway with its tunnels through the cliffs was built years later.)

Steven was the eldest of the four children in his family. He was fifteen years old at the time I was exposed to his penis. Small for his age, he'd had rheumatic fever as a child. He was handsome, though, as I have seen in old photos, with dark skin and curly black hair inherited from his Portuguese-Hawaiian father, an amateur musician whom my aunt had divorced to marry my Uncle Johnny. Steven and Johnny, who was Hawaiian-Haole-Chinese, didn't get along.

I was too young to understand the problems in my cousins' home. I adored Steven's sister Jill—seven years my senior. His brother Johnny-Boy, a couple of years younger than Jill, wasn't much on my radar. The youngest, Janis, was the same age as me—beautiful, with her father's light eyes and brown skin. But even at age five, I felt sorry for her. I overheard vague conversations between my mother and my grandmother, which always ended with "poor Janis." Perhaps she had ADHD or was simply a victim of a chaotic household (or both). But Janis was always getting into trouble. She also had a hearing problem as a child, which took a long time for anyone to figure out.

Shortly after arriving back in Honolulu, I went as a visitor to school with Janis. It was kindergarten, and the kids were taking naps. As I lay on my straw mat, I could hear Janis chattering and buzzing around the room, and the teachers telling her to settle down. I kept my eyes closed, pretending to be asleep. Then I heard one of the teachers say, "Janis, why can't you be good and behave like your cousin?"

My five-year-old brain thought, *Why do they have to say that to her? That's so mean.* It made me so, so sad at the time, and even as I write these words, tears come to my eyes.

In contrast, when I started kindergarten and then first grade at Lincoln School just down the hill from our house, my own experience was positive. I loved everything about school. Well, almost everything. The daily juice snack was a problem when it was that grainy guava nectar.

One night when Steven was staying with us in Honolulu, a middle-of-the-night call came from his mother. Rhetorically, because she already knew the answer, Auntie Connie asked my grandmother where Steven was, and to go check his bed. It was, of course, empty. Turns out he'd showed up in Lanikai after crashing Tutu's red Hillman on the Pali Highway. He had taken the tiny car when the rest of us were sleeping and had been coasting down the mountain to save gasoline when he lost control of the vehicle.

I'm sure that my mom and Tutu knew Steven was not okay and had problems beyond not getting along with his stepfather.

He was nice enough to me, though, or so I thought. We'd lie on my grandmother's double bed and watch the only television in the house. One day, he opened his pants and asked me to touch his penis (I don't think he called it that or called it anything at all)—and then to lick it. He wasn't threatening. It was just a request, and I did what he asked.

This happened more than once. I have tried over the years to recall more about the experience, but I can access neither the details nor any emotion I might have felt at the time. I wasn't repulsed, but I do remember thinking it was strange, and I knew somehow, I wasn't supposed to tell anyone about it. The incidents resurfaced for me a decade later, when we got the news that Steven had died in basic training in the Army. My mother was very sad, but I felt secretly relieved because it meant that the only person other than me who knew about what happened was gone.

Years later, as I became interested in American circumcision, I tried to recall whether Steven was circumcised or not, and I believe he was. Born in the early days of World War II, when Hawaii was a U.S. territory with enormous military presence in civilian life (including medicine), he would have fallen victim to the early wave of the practice, which—at the time—symbolized cleanliness and scientific medicine.

Chapter Three

THE DUKE OF SPARTA

As a child, I had little awareness of my family's immigrant history and how we fit into multi-ethnic Hawaii. I see now, though, how uniquely it colored my life. My grandmother's Greek was rudimentary. She arrived in San Francisco when she was only five or six, and over the years became far more comfortable in English, the language she spoke with my grandfather, despite him having arrived as a young adult. My Aunt Connie, six years older than my mother, ran with Hawaiian boys and other locals, could speak Pidgin, got pregnant young, and needed my grandmother's help to raise her four children from two marriages.

Because of all this, we lived more local style than my other Greek relatives who spoke Greek at home with their grandparents, had lots more money, and were more conservative politically than my mother and grandmother. My grandfather was atypical of the Greek men in Hawaii in that he never made any money (or maybe he made it and spent it irresponsibly), though he did buy that house in Makiki Heights.

Unlike our more affluent relatives, we didn't belong to the Oahu Country Club or the Outrigger Canoe Club. Tutu worked outside the home, first in my grandfather's restaurant, and then to pay off his debts after he passed away. For many years, she also played bridge "for money, not fun," to support herself and her daughters. During the years after we returned to live in Honolulu, she sold real estate. None of the other Greek women of her generation in Hawaii worked for money outside the home. Tutu's work ethic and independence impressed me at a very young age.

Greek dishes appeared regularly on our dinner table (moussaka, pastitsio, and sometimes lamb), along with more local dishes like "beef tomato" and the ubiquitous white rice eaten daily in Hawaii households. I never saw bread on the dinner table until I landed in New York City for college and ate regularly at Tom's, the neighborhood diner where *Seinfeld* was later filmed.

For holidays, birthdays, and other special occasions, we socialized with the other Greeks, some related by blood and others probably not. Those were the occasions when I remember my mother the happiest. She'd laugh heartily at her cousin Jimmy's tasteless jokes, which, coming from anybody else, would have annoyed, if not disgusted, her.

We also made an occasional trip to the Big Island of Hawaii, where my Great Uncle George Lycurgus was still alive, running and living at the Volcano House. Uncle George had been one of the first Greeks to settle in Hawaii. A legend to this day, he played an outsize role in popularizing Hawaii as a destination for intrepid travelers looking for adventure and exoticism.

Having left his small village near Sparta, and arriving in New York in 1877, he worked his way across the Mainland, (as people from Hawaii still refer to the continental U.S.), getting into the import business in California. Around 1890, the story has it, he stowed away (or, more likely, worked for his passage) on a cargo ship to Hawaii, and disembarked in Honolulu to try his fortune there.

In 1893, Uncle George opened the San Souci hotel and bar on the beach in Waikiki. Next, he visited the Big Island where, thirty miles to the west of the small port city of Hilo, he took over and managed a traveler's hostel on the edge of the Kilauea volcano crater. This edifice, rebuilt several times over the years, eventually became the present-day Volcano House, a rustic hotel in Volcano National Park.

The Big Island—and especially the rainforest area around the Kilauea crater and its bubbling Halemaʻumaʻu caldera—was the new Wild West, especially during Prohibition years. There was lots of money to be made, especially if one was motivated to succeed and perhaps a bit shameless.

Old photos from a biography written about him shortly after his death in 1960 show Uncle George in a three-piece white suit with a dark cummerbund, sporting a huge black moustache, and holding a cigar. Handsome and gregarious, he aligned himself with the Royalists, befriending the Hawaiian royal family and siding with them against the American businessmen and missionaries who were hoping to annex Hawaii as a U.S. Territory. He also hung out with rich and famous *haoles*, from the Carnegies to Mark Twain and Robert Louis Stevenson, who came through Hawaii on their way to adventures in Asia and Africa. Nicknamed the Duke of Sparta, Uncle George was charged with treason and briefly jailed for his support of the Hawaiian royal family.

On his first return visit to his native village in Greece in 1903, George Lycurgus met my great Aunt Athena, my grandfather's sister, and brought her back to Hawaii as his bride. He was forty-six, and she was nineteen. They went on to have three children—my auntie Tig (also called Georgina), and my uncles Nick and Leo. When Uncle George died in 1960, the local newspapers reported his age at 101, but my grandmother was skeptical: "The old man had no idea what year he was born," she told me. "Four or five years in a row, he threw himself a 75th birthday party."

My grandfather George Geracimos—I was his namesake—was the brother of Athena, Uncle George's young wife. Unlike his brother-in-law who helped him emigrate from Greece to Hawaii, George Geracimos wasn't much of a businessman.

According to my mother, her father loved the opera and art, and didn't care for politics though he always had liberal ideas. For a time, he owned the Waikiki Tavern, a restaurant right on the beach that's now crowded with hotels and shopping malls. My mother and my aunt Connie would go there after school and sit at the counter, imitating their father's Greek accent as he offered his patrons "appla pie" or "pitch [peach] pie."

In the early years of the Depression, my mother, my aunt, and Tutu spent a good deal of time "at the volcano"— Uncle George's Volcano House. Later, during World War II, they again spent time on the Big Island, staying at Volcano House or the Hilo Hotel, which the family also owned. "At least we could eat," my mother told me.

With all the young journalists off to war, my mother—who was enrolled in the prestigious Punahou School at the time—landed a job writing for the society page of the *Hilo Advertiser*, work that doubtless cemented her desire to major in English and become a college professor and writer.

Both my mother and my grandmother were important role models for my life and career. My mother had an extraordinary range of interests and the energy to pursue them. She eventually moved into college administration where she oversaw Hawaii Pacific University's academic programs on several military bases, interacting daily with high-ranking officers and enjoying every minute of those challenges, while teaching one or two courses a year. She also traveled to recruit students from the Western Pacific, wrote and served as editor for the *Hawaiian Journal of History* and was on the board of the Oahu Alliance for the Mentally Ill, and—just a few months short of her seventieth birthday—published her first book, a history of newspapers in Hawaii.

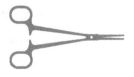

Chapter Four

EARLY LESSONS ON RACE, CLASS, AND COLONIZATION

T he Hawaiian Islands held a place in America's popular imagination as a far-off tropical paradise—an image advertised in the iconic Pan Am posters still sold to tourists today. But before jet travel, getting to and from Hawaii entailed a very long and expensive plane flight from the West Coast. For people who had money and were not in a hurry, there were luxury cruise ships that sailed between Honolulu and California or Honolulu and Australia. The voyage from Honolulu to Los Angeles or San Francisco took four and a half days.

On more than one occasion when my wealthy relatives sailed to the mainland on the first leg of a long journey back to Greece, we would go to the dock to see them off. We would watch the muscular young Hawaiian men dive for the coins (mostly silver half dollars) tossed by bystanders into the ocean as passengers were boarding the ship. There was great suspense every time—the coin glistening in the sunlight as it entered the water and began to sink, and the brown boys diving and jostling each other to be the first to retrieve it. They held the coins in their mouths, until they could take a break and stash them somewhere.

My mother loved Hawaii and felt it was a more open and racially tolerant place than much of the mainland United States. But by no means were "the islands" a bastion of social and racial equality. Throughout my childhood, my mother expounded upon the injustices suffered by native Hawaiians and successive waves of immigrants to Hawaii from Asia and the Pacific islands. As I learned more about the role of race, class, and colonization in American history, I realized how Hawaii's social ills are essentially American.

A curious exception occurred during World War II, when—unlike their counterparts on the Mainland—Japanese residing in Hawaii were allowed to remain in their homes and on their land. After reading David Guterson's novel *Snow Falling on Cedars* (about a formerly interned Japanese fisherman in Washington state accused of murder), I asked my mother why the Hawaiian Japanese had not been interned. She said, "There were simply too many of them; the economy would have fallen apart without them."

The three years I lived in Hawaii as a child gave root to so many of the themes that have motivated me throughout my life—even, in retrospect, my first primitive awareness of male sexuality. More generally, those years were when I first began to develop an awareness of social inequities, the importance of cultural identity, and a concern for justice. Details came to me over time, adding color to the complexity of my social consciousness. What, of course, I could not have known at the time was that the forced acculturation of Hawaiians involved forced male circumcision. Decades later, in 2002, I read in a historical snippet in the *Honolulu Advertiser* a tribute to Bill Kea, a prominent Hawaiian businessman who had just died at the age of 96. Kea was known to recount how as a boy attending Kamehameha Schools (a selective, private K-12 school for students with

Hawaiian ancestry), he woke up in great pain to find himself circumcised after being forcibly drugged with chloroform by school medical staff.[2]

Leaving was wrenching. Just weeks before our departure Hawaii became the 50th state. I remember the jubilant celebrations. Although I didn't understand what made statehood so important as a mark of "progress," I felt proud, identifying with more than my Texas birthplace. I took a lot of Hawaii with me when we departed in 1959. Despite the fact that I never returned to live there, nowhere else has ever truly felt like home to me.

Chapter Five
NEW MEXICO, NEW FATHER, NEW NAME

New Mexico wasn't unknown territory—to my mother or even to me since we had briefly lived in Santa Fe when my mother left my father to try her hand at writing.

In Albuquerque, I fell immediately for the Southwestern architecture at the University of New Mexico and its Museum of Anthropology just a few blocks on the other side of Route 66 from our rented house. I was intrigued by the Pueblos, the Navajo blankets displayed on the side of the road just a few miles west of the city, and the Native American dances we visited on holidays. I loved the sound of Spanish and other languages, and I loved the brown people, who reminded me of Hawaii.

And there was Petey, a Siamese-mix kitten we acquired within a few days of moving to Albuquerque. Not quite eight years old, I was in the third grade; Julia was in kindergarten. Walking home from school with my mother to our basement apartment, we stopped to watch a little Pekingese dog and a mid-sized kitten—black, white, and beige—playing in the front yard of one of the small stucco houses on our route. Right away, a lady came rushing out of the house. Would we like to have the kitten? Mom's answer was yes. I remember feeling that having a kitten was going to make life happy.

Albuquerque was where my mother met Hank, who was to become my new dad. Hank and my mom were both new graduate students in the English Department at University of New Mexico. In that first cramped apartment, Julia and I shared the one bedroom while my mom slept on the sofa-bed in the living room. More than once, I woke up at night because I heard her crying and calling out. I would wake her out of her nightmares. She must have felt very fearful and very alone, but she never talked with me about it.

The first time Julia and I met Hank was when he came to dinner one evening. We were sitting at the kitchen table with him while my mother served. She had sliced open and "buttered" the potatoes before putting them on our plates. Suddenly, Hank leapt out of his chair and spit a mouthful across the table. He started yelling something about margarine. Apparently, he despised the butter substitute, and my mother, who bought margarine because it was cheaper, did not know this important fact.

When my mom and Hank got married around a year later, we moved upstairs into the main part of the same house.

Our part of the house consisted of four rooms and a bathroom. My mom and Hank had the front bedroom, and Julia and I slept in the back bedroom. There was a nice living room, and a small kitchen with a door that led to the backyard which, in arid Albuquerque, was not much more than dirt and sand.

The margarine story remained a humorous family anecdote over the years, but I never thought it was funny. Hank's reaction was jarring and unpleasant and not a behavior my mother would have wanted her girls to think was all right. Ever sensitive to injustice, I felt it was insulting to my mother, who had invited him and put care into the meal she made for us all. This was a forerunner of other things that, over time, made me feel that pleasing Hank was something we all needed to prioritize—even when it made me feel bad about myself.

There were the lobster tails she'd buy for him on payday and the small Sara Lee cheesecakes, both of which, we were told, we wouldn't like. That might or might not have been true, but that wasn't the reason we didn't get to try them. The reason was money, which was in such short supply that there was no way I could be unaware of how much effort went into just scraping by.

There were the clothes I didn't get—like the pretty dresses and matching nightgowns Julia and I wore when we were children in Texas and Hawaii. In Albuquerque, my mother shopped from the Sears or Montgomery Ward catalog and bought me pants that were two sizes too big so I could "grow into them." They wore out long before that could happen.

I was relatively oblivious to how I looked in those clothes until one day a boy in my class named Danny asked me why my pants were so baggy. At a loss, I finally answered: "My pants aren't baggy." But I realized he was right, and I felt bad.

And there were the non-material slights, mostly having to do with my mother apparently feeling she needed to please Hank as thanks for taking her on—a woman several years his senior with two children.

When they got married, though, I was enthusiastic. I was too young to articulate, even to myself, my own needs, and I wanted my mom to be happy. She clearly wanted us all to live as a family, and so did he.

Hank planned to adopt us and the day after they married, I began using Chapin as my last name. I remember going to school clutching a note saying that I was no longer Georganne Arthaud. My new name was Georganne Chapin. I know everyone meant well, but since that day, I've never viewed taking a man's name as other than a vaguely debasing experience.

On the other hand, Hank greatly contributed to my intellectual development, introducing me to literature that certainly was not part of the fourth or fifth grade curriculum. He taught me some Spanish and imparted with great enthusiasm both opinions and knowledge that I later realized were not part of the growing-up years of most of my peers.

Thanks to Hank, I read Hemingway, Mark Twain, and John Steinbeck, Richard Wright and James Baldwin, and poetry by Conrad Aiken—about whom he would later write his doctoral dissertation. Also, we knew the poet Robert Creeley, who had gotten his MA from the same department where Hank and my mother were studying. Hank used to bribe me to read, promising a Dairy Queen hot fudge sundae for each novel, but that was more of a ritual than an incentive. I didn't need anything more than him putting a book in my hand for me to read it and then talk with me about it. In addition, around the time I was in fourth grade, Hank encouraged me to take private lessons to learn to play the flute, something that later gave me entrée into the world of South American folk music. He also helped to make me a candlestick costume for a Christmas parade, where I played my flute.

As I began writing this book and cycling through my memories, I sent a letter to Hank, asking him some questions about Albuquerque, and saying how I believe Albuquerque was when I truly started to become an adult. Here is some of what he wrote back:

A very warm letter. Thank you. Loved it! I just woke up, took Hoku and Dita out, fed them, and now I am settling down with the newspaper... But my inner wheels are turning about your thoughts of Albuquerque, which was a game changer for me too. I have lived in some pretty great places...

For now, there is one indisputable fact to corroborate your feeling about your transition at that time. As proof, when I arrived in 1959, you believed in Santa Claus. When we left in 1962 you did not.

Mom liked to entertain, and the evenings usually concluded after dinner with adjourning to the living room and discussing, discussing, and then discussing some more all things great and small. It was intelligent, interesting, honest and true, very grad school, with lots of wit, sophistication, and laughter. We often went to midnight with no problem. You always sat in on those discussions, which were a cut above the boring norm. You were quite interested and "got it." I'm sure you were positively influenced by the experience.

Love, Dad

Because Hank and my mother were on a nine-month grad school and teaching-assistant schedule, they had free time although no paychecks, during the summers. That's when we started visiting my new grandparents in Dobbs Ferry, New York. We'd leave Albuquerque in our blue VW bus and drive cross-country with our by-then-enormous Snowshoes Siamese cat Petey in a homemade crate in the back.

That first summer in Dobbs Ferry (1961), my new grandfather invited me to go to church with him. Grandma Jean wasn't interested in going, and Hank's younger brothers and sisters were similarly frying other fish. I truly loved walking down the hill hand in hand with Grandpa Henry to South Presbyterian Church, and Grandpa seemed to get as much enjoyment as I did out of our Sunday morning summer ritual. The stained-glass windows were awesome; the staid Presbyterian hymns were robust enough when accompanied with the church's big pipe organ (Grandpa told me he only sang in church because the organ and the rest of the congregation drowned out his off-pitch voice); and it was the first time I felt...I've had to search for the word...*comforted* since we'd left Hawaii two years earlier.

Chapter Six

MY BABY BROTHER IS CUT TWICE

My mother became pregnant with Chip during our last year in Albuquerque. She wasn't the one to tell me she was expecting a baby. She was never comfortable talking about sex, and, in retrospect, she probably thought it undignified to be pregnant at the age of 35. So, Mom deputized Hank to tell me first the so-called facts of life and, shortly thereafter, that she was expecting a baby. The former went something like this: "When a couple wants to have a baby, the man puts his penis into the woman's vagina." I'm pretty sure that was the first time I heard the word *vagina*, but I knew what he meant, so maybe he showed me some kind of diagram. I don't remember that part.

Having been thus schooled about how babies were made, a short time later Hank informed Julia and me that we were going to have a baby brother or sister.

"When did it happen?" I asked Hank.

He looked confused. "Well, the baby will be born in August," he answered.

"No," I insisted. "When did you put your penis into her vagina?"

He did some quick calculations and gave me an approximate month. I remember thinking, "How can he not remember something like *that?*"

Chip was born in North Tarrytown, now Sleepy Hollow, New York, near the end of a summer stay at my new grandparents' house. Hank's four younger siblings were still living at home or nearby, and Chip got a warm reception. I watched my mom change Chip's diaper. His penis looked very raw and angry red, a jarring sight in an otherwise perfectly smooth, pale new baby. But what did I know? Chip's penis was only the second one I'd ever seen.

Just a few days later, there was an emergency, and Chip had to be taken to the doctor quickly. When they came back, my mother was ghostly—more distraught and exhausted than I had ever seen her. Hank said something about her having to hold Chip while the doctor cut open the hole in his penis with a scalpel.

It wasn't until forty years later that I learned the technical term for what had happened to Chip. The opening of his penis through which urine passes had narrowed and then closed up. The condition, called *meatal stenosis*,[3] only happens to boys or men who have been circumcised.

Chip was just a couple of weeks old when we left Dobbs Ferry in the blue VW bus and drove the nearly 800 miles to Georgetown, Kentucky, which was to be our new home. Hank had gotten a position teaching English composition and literature at the University of Kentucky in Lexington, twenty miles south of Georgetown, and my mother had landed a similar post at Kentucky State College (later Kentucky State University), in the state capital Frankfort, twenty miles west.

From afar, I suppose, Georgetown seemed like a good choice, equidistant as it was between my parents' respective jobs—an example of the pattern of collaboration and mutual respect that continued for all the years they were married. Additionally, in the run-up to Georgetown, I distinctly remember them reassuring each other that Kentucky, which had never seceded from the Union in the Civil War, wasn't really the deep South.

Well, maybe not, but Georgetown in the early 1960s was plenty segregated. My three years there served as an early lesson in inequality, stigma, and discrimination. That town is where I learned the painful reality of how all these things deeply, albeit unconsciously, infused personal and social relationships.

It's safe to say that nobody in the family—least of all, me—had an inkling of what our lives would be like in Kentucky. If New Mexico marked the end of my childhood, the move to Georgetown marked a truly dangerous initiation into my adolescence. And if being taunted about my way-too-big-for-me baggy pants by a fifth-grade classmate in Albuquerque was a mini-lesson in ostracism, it paled in comparison to what I was to experience in Georgetown.

From day one, it was clear we didn't blend in. First, there was the blue Volkswagen bus. Nobody in Georgetown had a VW of any kind, let alone a Kombi which screamed non-conformity. Then there was Hank's beard. Nobody had one of those either, or if they did, they weren't a skinny white guy from New York who failed to observe the social divisions between Black and white.

Although Georgetown was a college town, the fundamentalist Christian Georgetown College—with its rules against dancing and card-playing on campus—meant that it had little in common with the secular and relatively progressive University of Kentucky and Kentucky State, a historically Black land grant college established in the late 19th century.

Then there was the way we talked. My first day of sixth grade, I was cornered by three girls, who demanded: "Say AH!"

"Ah," I repeated.

"No!" they yelled. "Say AH!!"

"Ah."

They then decided to give me a clue, without which this could have gone on for a lot longer. "Where'd y'all get that O-AYE?" one of them mimicked, twisting her mouth to approximate the way the word "I" sounded (to her) when it came out of my mouth.

Easy enough, I realized. I immediately began to pronounce I as "ah" instead of "eye" (which, of course, they also pronounced "ah").

The first house we lived in was a tiny rental on Bourbon Court. Scott County, Kentucky, where Georgetown was located, was "dry" (in other words, no liquor could be sold within the county limits), but Bourbon Court and Bourbon Street from which one turned on to Bourbon Court, apparently were named for more cheerful times.

Bourbon Court was all white and poor, with houses only a step up from mobile homes. Bourbon Street was Georgetown's version of a Black middle-class neighborhood, with solidly built houses occupied by their owners.

Looking back, I can't imagine how my mother did it. She had given birth less than a month earlier and was due to start a new teaching job as soon as we arrived in Kentucky. There was a household—however rudimentary—to set up. Schools had to be found for Julia and me. Food needed to be bought and meals prepared.

The way we lived in those days was one step up from camping. Very grad school, in retrospect, except that three of us five were children. We made do initially with a two-burner Coleman stove. I don't remember any babysitters at all during that time. Just as Mom and Hank compromised on location so they could have equal travel-time to their respective jobs, they arranged their schedules to work on opposite days, so someone would be home for us kids. Just as Julia and me before him, Chip was bottle- rather than breast-fed, so any of us could feed him.

We didn't stay long on Bourbon Court. The next stop was a much nicer house with a front yard on Clayton Street, just a block from the elementary school where I was enrolled in the sixth grade.

I don't remember any introduction, let alone a welcome, being accorded me as a new student. A day or two after the year began, my teacher Mrs. Smart delivered another language lesson to me, similar to my peers correcting my pronunciation of the first person singular. But this one was in social etiquette. I don't remember the question she asked me—maybe whether I'd finished my homework or had brought lunch, and I answered, "Yes."

"Yes, whut?" she shot back.

I was flummoxed. "Yes, I did," I replied.

"Yes, WHUT?" again. Then, seeing my genuine confusion, she helped me out: "Yes, ma'am!" she shouted, scowling. And then she scolded: "Yes, ma'am. That's how you answer me when I speak to you."

Mrs. Smart wasn't cruel. She just believed in teachable moments. And just as "Ah" had become an instant part of my vocabulary, I quickly began "ma'amming" and "sir-ring" all the grown-ups.

Of course, that wasn't enough. I'm pretty sure Mrs. Smart suspected, as I already knew, that fitting into Georgetown was not in my future.

A decade later, when I chose anthropology as my major in college, I realized that Georgetown was where I'd begun practicing "participant observation"—immersing myself and engaging in the activities of a culture, while maintaining the perspective of an outside observer or researcher.

Fifty years later, this is still pretty much how I roll.

Chapter Seven

UNCIVIL RITES

A nother big reason we stood out in Georgetown was that my family didn't go to church. Everyone in Georgetown belonged to one church or another, and one of the first things I remember people asking me in school was, "What are you?"—meaning what church did I go to?

Thanks to those Presbyterian Sunday mornings in Dobbs Ferry with my new grandfather, I had a handy answer: "Presbyterian."

The largest church in town was the huge brick Georgetown Baptist Church, with the First Christian Church coming in second. There was also an Episcopal Church built from stone, where my Girl Scout troop met. Georgetown's streets were lined with churches, large and small, white and Negro, formal and informal. Occasional tent revivals popped up here and there near our next rented house on Oak Street. None was integrated. Other than a boy named Jerry who was in the band and whose hand I once held on a hayride, I don't remember having any friends in my sixth-grade class. A girl from up the street named Linda invited me over once, but she didn't have much time to spend because her mother was very sick. She died later that year—the first time I remember a peer experiencing the death of a parent.

But I did make one friend in the neighborhood—Mrs. Hatfield, the widow on the corner opposite from our second rented house on Clayton Street. I don't remember how we met, but I ended up going there regularly. Mrs. Hatfield's husband had died recently, and she spoke a lot about him, and how much she missed him. She'd also just retired from playing the organ in a Baptist church and talked about that, too. What she spoke the most about was how her late husband was with the Lord and how the Lord was also with her, and they'd all be together again one day. I'd enjoyed going to church with my grandfather and knew about God, but I'd never heard anyone who had such a personal relationship with the Lord.

Mrs. Hatfield invited me to sit next to her on the piano bench and taught me hymns. There was some overlap with what the Presbyterians were singing in Dobbs Ferry, New York, but not much. This was serious Baptist Bible-thumping music: "Onward Christian Soldiers," "He Lives," and the sadder "Old Rugged Cross." We sang them together, Mrs. Hatfield and me, every afternoon that I could make my way over to her house after school.

One day, my mother and Hank told me they thought it wasn't right for me to be spending so much time with Mrs. Hatfield—something about how I should have activities with girls my own age. But the real reason, I'm sure, was that they didn't like me being subjected to Mrs. Hatfield's southern Baptist indoctrination. They did not seem to understand that it wasn't the religion lessons, but rather the music, Mrs. Hatfield's loneliness, and her kindness toward me that kept me going back.

Two other things stand out in my memories of sixth grade. First, I joined the high school marching band, which—because band was not cool among Georgetown's high schoolers—relied on younger kids to fill its ranks.

The other was that my sister Julia got her own dog. Julia always loved animals, especially horses and dogs. She had run into a boy her age, eight years old, who lived half a block away, and he told her his parents wanted to find a home for their small brown and white girl dog, named Chaser. Julia told the boy she would ask her parents. Hank and my mom agreed, but the next day when Julia went to claim Chaser, the boy told her a man had come and arranged to take her. Julia was devastated, until she returned home in tears and discovered that the man who'd spoken for Chaser was...Hank! Just as with Petey, the cat we adopted when we first arrived in Albuquerque, pets have always been a source of unconditional comfort and love in my sister's and my lives.

The Baptist indoctrination "problem" took care of itself—to the satisfaction of my parents, at least—when we moved back across town to Oak Street the summer of 1963, just before seventh grade. I never saw my piano-thumping, hymn-singing friend again. Even today, I think about how abandoned she must have felt and regret that I never went to visit her again.

Part of the reason for this was that my life was becoming more and more complicated. Everyone in town knew about my parents' civil rights activities. I had joined the Girl Scouts, and Julia was a Brownie. At a local civil rights meeting, my mom had met another mom—a Black woman named Mrs. Peters—and they discovered they were each leading a Brownie troop, one "Negro" and one "white." They decided to merge the two. I'm pretty sure the Brownies didn't mind, but my mother's actions further contributed to the Chapins' reputation among the Georgetown establishment as dangerous weirdos—the VW bus, Hank's beard, non-churchgoers, and disrespectful, in general, of the social order.

And white Georgetown didn't know the half of it: Hank was bringing home radical material, like Bob Dylan's first LP, released in early 1962. And Pete Seeger's version of "We Shall Overcome." And Sam Cooke's "A Change Is Gonna Come." I had no one outside the family with whom I could share this miracle music, but I was enthralled. Most folk music has its roots in protest—movements against social injustice—and manifests people's emotional connections with the land and with their roots. These themes would later draw me into international folk music and my eventual marriage to a socially conscious, working-class Argentine folk musician. But in 1960s Georgetown, I kept as much as I could about my family's heretical activities under wraps. I just wanted to be accepted.

I could never pretend to be a Baptist; the absence of my parents in church would have been a dead giveaway that there was something wrong with me. But I made my way to the First Presbyterian Church and was welcomed there. It wasn't a large church, especially not when compared to Georgetown Baptist, but it was respectably located on Main Street, and I remember feeling acceptance and even kindness. I started going to Sunday school, joined a youth group, and was even asked to sing a solo ("O' Holy Night") at a Christmas service.

That was the same Christmas season when a boy named Steve—out of nowhere and when no one was looking—smashed his index finger hard into my left breast as we were caroling with the youth group early one evening. I remember to this day the pain and shock I felt, and also how impossible it seemed to confront him or tell anybody what he'd done.

My church was a fifteen-minute uphill walk from Oak Street, and some Sundays Hank would drive me. In the car and then after we got home, Hank would wax eloquent on the hypocrisy of Christianity, pointing out that the white "so-called Christians" in Georgetown were segregationists. I could certainly see his point, but at the time I didn't understand what any of that had to do with me going to the Presbyterian Church where, unlike in school, nobody called me names and they let me sing.

Despite his impatience at the time with organized religion, Hank was active in the Civil Rights Movement, which was closely linked to Black churches in the South. He certainly respected the Black ministers and others who organized and led the protests and demonstrations.

My mother was never stridently pro- or anti-religion. But the churning conflict I felt between functioning at home and finding acceptance in a place that was downright hostile to people like us meant that the three years in Georgetown, a blip on the screen in my parents' trajectory, carved out a disproportionately large space in my psyche.

My newest school, located in the south end of town, served students in grades seven through twelve. It was a half-hour walk from Oak Street, and usually Hank drove me in the mornings, and I'd mosey my way home in the afternoon. Winters weren't particularly harsh in Georgetown, but during one extreme cold spell, Hank realized that some of the Black kids from our neighborhood were walking to school without hats or gloves or warm coats. He began offering them a ride in the blue VW bus.

I knew this was a compassionate thing to do, but I also knew I was going to pay the price. So, as we were nearing the school, I'd put forth some lame reason he should let me walk the last couple of blocks. He paid no attention and, sure enough, the drop-off (three Black kids and me) at the main door of the school resulted in a new nickname for me, which I won't repeat here, a term used by southern racists to describe a white person (particularly a "Yankee"), who associated with Black people. The bullies' words in and of themselves didn't hurt me because I had heard many adult discussions by my parents and their friends about the mentality of people who used derogatory racist terms. Hank was living his principles, which was a good example for me. But as an adolescent, it irritated me that he would create one more obstacle for me to overcome as an outsider trying to adapt to a new school environment.

Some of the actions people took were quite sinister. One afternoon as I headed home on foot, a big white Chevy convertible pulled up to the curb. I knew some of the kids in the car, and the driver—a boy a couple grades ahead of me—asked if I wanted a ride. I stepped over to the car, which was still rolling slowly. As I grabbed the handle of the back door, he sped off with the occupants of the car shouting my new nickname. Even telling the story today, I recall the terror I felt as I let go of the handle to keep from being dragged down the street. I never told my parents.

Another day, my family was eating dinner in the Oak Street house when a glass bottle hurled from a passing car came crashing through front window, accompanied by shouted curses about my family's affection for Black people. Everybody was shaken, but nobody was injured. I believe the police were called, but no action was taken. Incidents like these were commonplace in the South (and even some places in the North) at that time.

I knew that being popular in Georgetown was out of reach. I also knew my parents' commitment to racial integration and fairness was the only defensible position to take. Although I never had disdain for my Black neighbors or schoolmates, I do confess that I often tried to distance myself from my parents. The familiar longing to fit in welled up and sometimes overtook the pride I felt in my parents' stance.

While we were living on Oak Street, one day my grandmother called from Honolulu to tell my mother that my cousin Steven had died during basic training in the Army. My mother was very sad—Steven was her sister's troubled eldest son—whereas I had conflicted feelings because of what he had encouraged me to do on Tutu's bed while watching TV.

Three decades later, during a visit to Hawaii when I was in my 40s, I told Hank what Steven had done to me. He apparently told my mother, because she brought it up the next day, telling me she was very sorry and that she had no idea. Then she added, almost as an afterthought, that the reason Steven had been sent to stay with us in Honolulu was because my Uncle Johnny had caught him molesting my cousin Janis who was exactly my age. In addition to sparking feelings of betrayal, I was struck by my mother's and grandmother's blindness to the threat that Steven's behavior with his sister posed for me and my sister, not to mention the effect it may have had on Janis's troublesome behavior at school and elsewhere.

Denial by adults regarding harm inflicted on the children they love would become all too familiar to me in my work against infant circumcision.

Chapter Eight
ALL THE WAY

I spent a lot of time out of the house in whatever group activities I could find. I met a girl from one street over. Betsy was pretty with dark wavy hair and blue eyes, and her family was poor. Betsy and I used to walk around the neighborhood singing popular songs like the Dixie Cups' "Chapel of Love," switching off the melody and harmony lines.

I stayed in Girl Scouts. I played my flute in the high school band. I learned to be a scorekeeper for the baseball team, and I kept going to the Presbyterian Church. I managed to find a few sort-of-popular girls who were willing to hang out with me in a limited way. I'd skip lunch so I could stop by the drug store with them, sit in a booth and order a chocolate marshmallow sundae. The few moments of feeling like I belonged more than made up for my mother's suspicion when I arrived home still hungry, having eaten no real food since breakfast.

The main thing I remember about seventh grade, aside from my racially integrated busing experience, courtesy of Hank, was my Kentucky state history class. It was taught by a tall, skinny young teacher named Mr. Klein. Mr. Klein liked to paddle errant students. What qualified as errant was somewhat of a mystery, especially since most of the students he paddled were girls whose worst transgression was giggling or talking in class. Mr. Klein would have the offender bend over his desk at the front of the room where the entire class had a view. Then he'd wallop them on the behind with a wooden paddle with holes in it. This spectacle took place every couple of days throughout the school year.

Each time I'd squirm in my desk and feel my face flush. I don't think Mr. Klein hit anyone very hard. And, as far as I know, no one ever reported his questionable disciplinary approach to their parents. Although I may have blocked it out, I don't think the creep ever paddled me. But time has taught me that unpleasant events and trauma can punch holes in one's memory.

The first couple of years we lived in Georgetown, both the drug store soda fountain and a luncheonette across the street called The Cardinal were semi-segregated. Black people could order food to take out but couldn't sit down in either establishment to consume the food they'd just paid for. How insulting.

This changed shortly before we left Georgetown, in the wake of several years of Civil Rights legislative efforts and demonstrations. A major catalyst was a huge march in Frankfort following the refusal of the Kentucky legislature to pass the federal Civil Rights Act of 1964. Martin Luther King and Jackie Robinson spoke at the peaceful protest.

In 1965, a conference on Civil Rights was held in Louisville to address employment and public accommodations. Shortly thereafter, Georgetown's sit-down lunch counters and drugstore opened to Black people. I remember being in a booth at the drugstore with my nickel coke and chocolate marsh (a sundae made with chocolate ice cream and marshmallow cream) and seeing a group of Black girls sit down in the adjacent booth where only the day before this would have been impossible. A sense of immense relief washed over me.

The other world event that occurred when I was in eighth grade was the assassination of President Kennedy. It happened in the afternoon during my favorite class: band. We didn't have a television in the band room. The principal announced over the loudspeaker that the President had been shot. A lot of us started to cry.

Strangely, with one exception, I do not remember the names of my bandmates. The exception is a kid named Nicky. His father owned a small grocery store, and Nicky worked there behind the counter after school and on weekends. Before I knew him, he had lost a finger to a meat slicer. But you didn't need five fingers to play his instrument, a shorter version of the trumpet called a cornet.

Two decades after leaving Georgetown, as I began to speak out against circumcision and the damage it created, I'd flash on Nicky. I thought about how he functioned with that missing finger, but also how nobody would have disputed the fact that Nicky had lost something important— a finger. In contrast, the pushback intactivists get when we point out that circumcised men are missing something important (their normal and exquisitely sensitive foreskins) strikes me as beyond ironic. The naysayers' argument: Circumcised men "can still have an orgasm." I am certain nobody ever said to Nicky, "What are you complaining about? You can still play the cornet."

Although Georgetown was an inhospitable place for me, the odd gift living in that town gave me was excellent preparation for taking on unpopular causes. Day-to-day life, though, was downright dangerous for adolescent girls. Sex was everywhere, and I still didn't know anything more than the "penis in the vagina" baby-making story. My classmates' older sisters were getting pregnant at the age of fifteen, sixteen, or seven-teen, and then (usually) married immediately after the pregnancy became obvious. A more unusual twist of this story, this one promulgated by the mean girl of the seventh grade when the misfortune befell her older sister, was that the couple had been secretly married before engaging in the sex act. *Why, if she was married, would she be having sex in the backseat of a car?* I wondered.

There was one girl, though, whose pregnancy had a different ending. She was from a prominent local family (I won't give any more details, because finding her on Facebook tells me she is still very much a part of the local establishment). She became pregnant when she was thirteen years old. The whispered story was that her parents took her somewhere out of the country for an abortion. I believe that's the first time I heard the word abortion, and I don't remember who explained it to me, but it left an impression on me—mostly about how she, whose parents were affluent, had an option that other teenage girls in town did not.

Sometime during that last year in Kentucky at the age of thirteen I got my first boyfriend. He was the younger brother of the guy who was going steady with that same mean queen of the seventh grade. I suppose that was for me some attenuated association with royalty. My boyfriend's name was Barry. He was in the ninth grade and played baseball. I met him through my job as the team's scorekeeper. Soon, we too were going steady, as represented by the cheap man's ring he gave me which—in the style of the day, in Georgetown, anyway—I wrapped in angora yarn, fluffed up with a toothbrush and proudly wore on my ring finger.

It wasn't long before we began kissing, and then "petting"—though the latter mostly consisted of him groping me here and there. I do not remember being sexually aroused, or maybe I simply was too clueless to identify it as such. I mostly remember wanting him to like me and not wanting to get caught by my parents. Barry was too young to have a driver's license, so our moments of opportunity were few and far between.

One day, during my last summer in Georgetown, Barry and I went to a drive-in movie. We did what other young teens did in similar circumstances: We spread a blanket on the ground in front of the car whose occupants had given us a ride. There in the shadow of the hood where we thought nobody could see us, we started making out. I remember hearing the movie from the speakers of other cars around us.

The next thing I knew, he had pulled down my pants and was forcing himself inside me. The pain was awful, but the episode didn't last more than a minute or two. When I got home, my panties were stained with still-wet blood. And that was how I lost my virginity, though the only words I had to acknowledge the experience were that we'd gone "all the way."

We went all the way fairly frequently over the next couple of months. I began to feel extremely anxious. Although I knew very little about the mechanics of conception, I knew with terrible certainty that plenty of other girls who had gone all the way were getting pregnant.

When we were having sex, I used to ask Barry, "Can we stop now?"

He'd respond, "I just have to wait until I get this feeling."

I didn't know what feeling he was talking about, but I did know that prolonging the act was not enjoyable for me.

In some inchoate way, I also understood that my family didn't have the money or the savvy of the school board member who took his daughter for an abortion. And marrying Barry was definitely a no-go. So, for the last few months before we moved away, anxiety consumed me.

Years later, when I read Ann Fessler's book *The Girls Who Went Away,*[4] about young, unmarried women who were coerced into giving up their babies for adoption during the 1950s and 1960s, I had to keep putting it down to fight off panic and tears. Becoming pregnant in Kentucky at the age of thirteen would have launched me into a cascade of tragedies. My mother is no longer alive, but when Hank reads these words, it will be the first time he learns of how narrow my escape from disaster was when we left Georgetown. Late in the summer of 1965 as we drove north on the newly opened interstate 75 toward Yellow Springs, Ohio, I felt enormous relief. Through no particular intelligence or purposeful action of my own, I had managed to dodge bottles thrown through our windows, bullies, and sperm cells.

Chapter Nine

GROOVING TO THE OFFBEAT

While my parents had settled on Georgetown, Kentucky, because it was convenient to their jobs, they selected our next hometown, Yellow Springs, Ohio, because it met their criteria for political liberalism and an interesting place to live.

Yellow Springs had been famous for its progressive social history and racial integration since the mid-1800s. Home of Antioch College, the town was an oasis of culture and left-leaning intellectual thought in the middle of Ohio farmland. Most important for me, just heading into high school, Yellow Springs gave me permission to ask questions and explore my own thoughts, beliefs, and principles outside the context of my immediate family.

I was thirteen, Julia was ten, and Chip was just turning three when we made the trip from Georgetown. Julia rode with Hank in the moving truck, holding her two pet rats—Long Evans and Minnie—in a cage on her lap. Petey Cat, Chaser the dog, Chip, and I traveled with my mom in the VW bus. The distance from Georgetown to Yellow Springs was only 140 miles. The contrast between the two places, however, revealed in microcosm the ideological conflicts, economic and social inequities, and racial strife underlying the history of our country. Even then, at thirteen years old, I felt both participant in and witness to deep and consequential forces and events and knew these would shape my future.

Yellow Springs stood out as an anomaly both politically and demographically in south-central Ohio. In other ways, it was pure rural Midwest. My classmates at Yellow Springs High School, whose student body numbered slightly more than four hundred students, were evenly distributed among rural farm kids, kids whose parents owned or worked in local small businesses, the offspring of college professors, and those from a handful of relatively affluent families who owned construction and manufacturing businesses in town. I fell into the third group, but we all knew and interacted with each other. And unlike in Georgetown, where suppressing my parents' principled positions and my own personal values was a prerequisite for avoiding conflict and meanness, Yellow Springs thrived on open-mindedness, sometimes confusingly or maddingly so.

The relocation to Yellow Springs also meant we were moving up in the world, marked by the fact that my parents became homeowners. Through a series of machinations, including a small personal loan from Dorothy, the real estate agent (who remained a family friend), they managed to buy an old four-bedroom house on Dayton Street—one of the village's two main thoroughfares. I had the upstairs front bedroom with windows on three sides that I adorned with three rows of curtains—the bottom hot pink, the middle pale pink, and the top white. The inspiration was more Georgetown than Yellow Springs, though I'd shed Barry's ring with the pink mohair when we'd left.

Because Yellow Springs offered a lot more of interest than curtains, the décor stayed through my high school years and my transformation into a hippie chick. With my new look, I wore my hair down my back and a funky wardrobe I mostly sewed myself. The general store in town had a reasonable fabric section, good for my A-line skirts, skimpy shift dresses, and colorful inserts I used to turn my Levi's into psychedelic bell-bottoms.

As a freshman at Yellow Springs High School, I quickly jettisoned my Kentucky accent. It took me some time, though, to figure out the social dynamics. I remember looking around at my new classmates seated on the bleachers in the gym as the principal welcomed us all on the first day, and wondering, *Who are the popular girls here?* Having only Georgetown to go by, the girls I surmised fit into that category were the few who were wearing make-up and wore their hair in a flip. I would soon find out that these features didn't equate to academic success or social engagement at Yellow Springs High School.

Because the school was so small, YSHS had no formal academic tracking, no advanced placement courses, and only minimal social segregation within the student body. The main exception was freshman science. Because I was new, I ended up in the general science class, taught by a man who tripled as the junior varsity basketball coach and part-time school bus driver.

Before we left Georgetown, Hank had cautioned me that I might find myself outclassed academically in Yellow Springs—a small fish in a bigger intellectual pond. He would say the same thing four years later when I entered Barnard College. I know now he meant well. I suspect he didn't want me (and perhaps himself) to be disappointed if I couldn't keep up with the towering high school intellects in a progressive college town. But I continued my pattern of being at the top of my class.

Certain things that had been uncool in Georgetown, like band, were a source of pride in Yellow Springs. While football was a big deal in Georgetown, Yellow Springs had no high school football team, so there was no marching band but rather a top-notch concert band. I played in the flute section for my entire four years. We traveled around the state for concert band competitions, always doing well, and relishing our offbeat Yellow Springs identity. From that time, I've loved to get on the road or in a plane and check out different places and people—near or far, it doesn't matter.

Most dramatic, though, was the atmosphere of racial tolerance and integration in Yellow Springs. The stress and anxiety I had felt in Kentucky related to my parents' civil rights work simply evaporated.

For a town of 4,000, Yellow Springs offered an astonishing range of activities and options for engagement. The Little Art Theatre, a five-minute walk from our house, showed first-run American movies, as well as more esoteric foreign films. There was also community theatre, a natural foods co-op, and a fine, independent weekly newspaper that liberally printed the opinions of local residents. The Village Bakery, next to the movie theatre, made incredibly delicious whole wheat donuts, and any late night out included a stop to buy some when the bakery opened at 2 a.m. In email correspondence following our graduating class's 50th reunion, Sterling "Skeeter" Wright, a star in Yellow Springs High School basketball, recounted bringing home teammates from the professional team he later played with in France. The highlight of their visit, he reported, was the donuts.

Many of Antioch's campus activities were open to the public, and some of us townies interacted a lot with the college students, staff, and faculty. One of the things I enjoyed most was the outdoor folk-dancing, which exposed me to a huge range of international folk music—laying a foundation for my later avocation.

Yellow Springs also boasted a fantastic horseback riding center. My sister Julia, who had been obsessed with horses since she was a young child, acquired her first horse, named Nugget, when she was in middle school. She paid for Nugget's board by delivering the Xenia Daily Gazette door-to-door and collecting from customers weekly. Her boss told my mom, "I'm not supposed to hire a girl, but I am going to anyway." I didn't share Julia's passion for horses or riding, but I appreciated then, as I do now, my parents' willingness to encourage that passion and the career it led to. In 1993, Julia established the Northwest Therapeutic Riding Center in Bellingham, Washington. Still active today, the center offers riding lessons to people of all ages and abilities and has provided meaningful work experience for hundreds of volunteers over the years.

In short, Yellow Springs was a place rich with ideas, options, and possibilities. Because of vibrant Antioch College, the town hosted an ever-changing cast of characters from the literary world, politics, and the natural and social sciences. Both faculty and the many visitors to the campus were activists committed to the most prominent social justice issues of the day. My high school years, 1965 to 1969, coincided with one of the most intense periods of social change in American history, and left-leaning Yellow Springs encapsulated many forces of the revolution, where conflicts abounded, and original thinking was encouraged and rewarded. I wish every young person could have the experience of growing up in such a place.

Chapter Ten

BROTHER FROM ANOTHER MOTHER

Shortly after moving to Yellow Springs, Hank and my mom had begun to talk about adopting another child, a boy. In part, this was to give my brother Chip a sibling close to his age, as my sister and I were, respectively, seven and ten years older. But they were also intrigued by interracial adoption, which was becoming a thing in the mid-1960s. They decided to adopt a Black child.

I recall very little of the preparations leading up to the appearance of a new son and brother in our home, though I certainly was on board. But sitting in algebra class the day before he was to arrive, I was seized with an anxiety bordering on terror. *What if I don't love him? What if I can't love him?*

The next day, in early January 1967, a sixteen-month-old baby joined our household. He'd been living in a foster home since shortly after his birth and the social worker from the adoption agency brought him to us. The minute I saw this chubby-cheeked, dark-eyed boy come through the door in her arms, I felt an overwhelming rush of tenderness. I thought he was the most beautiful child I'd ever seen.

The agency that handled the adoption told my parents that the baby's father was in the military and his mother was young and couldn't take care of him on her own. His birth name—the first name was all the agency revealed—was Howard. My parents changed it to Nicholas, after numerous Greek uncles and cousins from my mother's family, and they selected the middle name Douglass, after the famous Black abolitionist Frederick Douglass.

We were all in love with the new member of our household. But Nicky himself was dubious. He and Chip shared a room, Chip in a single bed against one wall and Nicky in a crib against the opposite wall. The hardwood floors were uncarpeted, and at night, Nicky would rock himself so hard that his crib would travel around the room. And for some time after coming to us, when he'd call out "Mommy" in the morning and my mother would go to him, he would stand holding the railing and shriek as if to say, "No! You are not my mommy!"

I wondered then, *What must it be like for a baby to be taken away—first from his birth mother, and then from a foster family with whom he'd lived for nearly a year-and-a-half? How could anything have prepared him for being relinquished a second time, even though that was in the cards all along?*

I also wondered if, when his mother gave him up, she had been told there was no permanent home lined up for him. Years later, I read in an edition of the Boston Women's Collective's *Our Bodies, Ourselves* that a mother giving up her son for adoption had the right to consent to his circumcision. I wondered whether Nicky's mom had agreed to have him cut, or if she was told at all.

I wonder now, if my parents had kept Nicky in their room, whether they might have been able to comfort him in the middle of the night. Might his transition have been easier? What must it have been like for him to be among strangers who were calling him Nicky, instead of his birth name Howard, which he'd answered to for his entire life until the day he came to our home?

Did anybody even think about these questions at that time? Probably not. Those were the days of nurture versus nature, and the expectation that well-meaning adults and "a good home" could cancel out any losses or trauma a child might have suffered in the past. It was the same clean-slate kind of thinking that allowed parents to believe doctors who cut off part of their sons' penises, reassuring them, "He won't remember a thing."

In the spring of 1968, we all went to court the day Nicky's adoption was to be finalized. Martin Luther King, Jr. had been assassinated only a few days earlier. My parents decided to change Nicky's new intended middle name yet again, from Douglass to King. Sitting in the waiting room with us was a couple there for the adoption of their little blonde daughter. The receptionist asked her, "Where did you get those big blue eyes?" The child answered in a practiced sing-song voice, "God gave them to me."

The participant observer in me noted the heavy roles and expectations being placed by former strangers onto these tiny children—the child whose blue eyes had been given to her by God, and my brown brother now bearing the first name of a dozen Greeks in my mother's family, the middle name of a Black civil rights martyr, and the last name of a renowned 17th century New England Puritan.

Only six years had passed since my own name change and adoption by Hank, and only four years since Chip's birth and two immediate genital surgeries. Even though the details of our lives and our losses were distinct, I related deeply to my two brothers. I am certain that these observations, these feelings, and these relationships are at the root of the compassion and empathy I have drawn upon to work effectively with circumcision survivors and their loved ones.

***

Around the time Nicky came into our family, I began waiting tables at the Antioch Inn, the restaurant owned by the college of the same name. Except for a couple of taverns, "the Inn" was the only sit-down eating establishment in Yellow Springs. Everyone went there, including Antioch students and staff, townspeople, and blue-haired ladies who came from Springfield or Xenia to dine after church on Sundays. This latter group of patrons might have enjoyed the food, but they looked askance at the long-haired college students and mini-skirted waitresses like me.

Working at the Inn, I became friendly with many Antioch students—including a group of budding revolutionaries, several who later became well-known in radical leftist circles. These college students viewed us middle-class high school waitresses as oppressed workers and left us enormous tips in cash or college meal tickets that could be used another day at the Inn or in the campus cafeteria.

Up to that time, I had associated political activism with my parents, their colleagues, and their civil rights and anti-war activities. Here, though, was a group of students only slightly older than me who were already deeply interested in broad social justice issues. These acquaintances opened my eyes to human rights as an overarching concept that included the lives and rights of poor people, of women, of immigrants, and of those who labored under horrible conditions for horrible wages.

Despite Antioch's inclusiveness and liberal ideology, all was not harmonious on campus or in town. In the mid-1960s, Antioch had begun recruiting students from around the country to study in a new

Black-students-only program called the Afro-American Studies Institute. In 1968, the college established a dorm called Unity House, reserved for Black students who were part of that program. Some of the Unity House residents seemed considerably older than the eighteen- to twenty-two-year-olds who were the norm for an undergraduate residential college. Some of them carried guns. The liberal faculty and administration were in over their heads.[5] They weren't the only ones.

One evening as I was finishing my shift at the Inn, a group of four Unity House students walked through the door. The hostess—a Black woman from town named Sherri—told them the kitchen was closed but offered to seat them if they wanted dessert and coffee. When I went to their table, they insisted on ordering dinner and demanded that I bring the paper slips the Inn gave to customers to fill in their choices.

I repeated what the hostess had said—that the kitchen had closed at 7:30. (This was small-town Ohio, remember.) "You won't be able to order dinner, but I can bring you coffee and dessert," I said, feeling a bit uneasy.

There was a lot of grumbling, and a short, stocky woman in the group got loud. "You better go back to that kitchen now and get our dinner," she shouted.

I was nervous but also vaguely amused at the thought of sixteen-year-old me walking into the back and telling the tough union workers in the kitchen to reopen the serving table for a bunch of college students. I repeated, "The kitchen is closed. There's nothing I can do about it."

I had no time to step back even an inch as she jumped up, cocked her arm, and slugged me square in my left jaw.

I don't remember what happened next—only that a few minutes later, I was standing at the reception desk holding a wet napkin to my face. The place had cleared out. Neither Sherri nor anyone else called or mentioned notifying the police or campus security. No one asked me if I wanted to make a report.

And when I reached home and told my parents what had happened, they offered me sympathy. But they, too, weren't about to call the cops or file a complaint with the college about the woman who'd assaulted their daughter. That would, in their book, have been racist.

I, on the other hand, was incensed that someone could punch me in the face and get away with it because I wasn't able to give her what she wanted. I believed that if my assailant had been white, my parents' response would have been different. To me, this represented not racial tolerance, but rather fear and an inability to confront on an individual level the contradictions inherent in a racist culture.

We see the same kind of cognitive dissonance that allows people to condemn the genital cutting of girls while condoning the genital cutting of boys. If we are to achieve justice, it can never be by favoring one class of victim or victimizer over another. These conversations all started in my head when I was a young girl, and—though imperfectly—Yellow Springs began preparing me to hold and work through multiple contradictory forces and ideas in the years to come.

PART TWO: IDENTITY

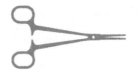

Chapter Eleven
A CERTAIN IMAGE

My parents' liberalism on race did not extend to other contemporary issues—specifically, drugs and sex. They despised the former and were downright prudish about the latter, especially when it came to me.

The summer after my junior year in high school, I got involved with a guy a couple of years older than me. Pretty much everyone called him Head because he smoked a lot of pot. He was born Prentiss Tomas in New York City, and his father, who was Black, died when he was a baby. His white mother, whose name was Beulah, brought him to Yellow Springs because she believed it would be a good place to raise her interracial child.

A few years later, Beulah married Horace Champney, a big-time peacenik who opposed the Vietnam War. Prentiss ended up using Champney as his last name, just as I had ended up using Chapin.

Despite the popularity of his nickname, I never called Prentiss "Head." Neither was I ever much into pot. But we did have sex, and I did take psychedelic drugs a few times with him and other friends who hung out at his house We also spent time in the Vale, a rural counterculture enclave a couple of miles outside town.

My parents were conflicted about my relationship with Prentiss, but not because of his race. They remained active in civil rights and anti-war activities, and our home was a regular gathering spot for activists, black and white, including some questionable characters. But, understandably, I suppose, their tolerance didn't automatically extend to my own personal life and choices of friends.

Hank and my mom didn't suspect I was smoking pot or using other drugs, because I had no trouble doing my schoolwork and maintaining good grades. They also liked and respected Prentiss's mom. Everyone did. And they knew the saintly Horace, like many crusaders, was a very difficult person, and probably figured (correctly) that he wasn't very nice to his troubled stepson.

But Prentiss was too quiet, too sullen, and maybe even too tall for them to feel comfortable. He rode a black BMW motorcycle, wore high black leather boots, and carried a huge Hasselblad camera everywhere. He shot photos of everyone and published some of them in a leftist local newspaper called *The Independent Eye*. Once, he came over to shoot pictures of my younger brothers. When he went to develop the photos, there wasn't any film in the camera. He was so stoned he'd forgotten to load it.

One summer night, just after I'd gone to bed, my mother came to my room. The weather was hot, and I was sleeping nude—but pulled the sheets up to my neck as she knocked and opened the door. Seeing my bare arms, she asked, "Are you wearing a nightgown?"

"No, Mom, it's too hot," I answered.

My mother flushed, visibly upset, and practically spit out her next words: "Why are you such an exhibitionist?"

I didn't answer but thought: *That's absurd. I was alone in my own room with my door closed before you knocked and came in without even waiting for me to respond.*

Mom sat down next to me on the bed. "Dad and I don't approve of your relationship with Prentiss," she said.

"But I love him," I answered her.

After a brief silence, she took a deep breath and muttered, "God help you."

Then she got to the point. "I need to tell you if you get pregnant with an interracial baby after Dad and I adopted Nicky...," she paused, looking away from me. "I just don't know what we would do."

That last sentence hung in the air and reverberated in my brain: "I just don't know what *we* would do."

Though her words were vague, the meaning was clear: Me getting pregnant would both embarrass my parents and cancel out the good deed they had undertaken to perform by adopting my youngest brother. Missing from her admonition was even a single word having to do with me, or consideration for my situation. This, like my parents' failure to defend me after I was assaulted at the Antioch Inn, was one of many times that I felt abandoned by my mother.

I knew she loved me, but her desire to convey a certain image about our family seemed a greater priority than trying to understand and support me, her adolescent daughter. The truth was that my relationship with the troubled Prentiss had become a problem for me, too, but at this point, I felt I couldn't trust my mom with that information.

With regard to getting pregnant, though, luckily some of my Vale friends had mothers who had educated them, and they educated me in turn. Prentiss had no problem using condoms, and a visit to a gynecologist in nearby Xenia resulted in a prescription for birth control pills, hidden just a few feet from where my mom and I had the conversation about Prentiss that night. I'd stashed the pills on my bookshelf between pages of the John Steinbeck novel *The Winter of Our Discontent*. I knew they'd be safe there because my parents had mentioned they felt Steinbeck's later books were decidedly inferior to his earlier works, and thus wouldn't be tempted to borrow my copy. So that night I could truthfully tell my mother, "I'm not going to get pregnant." She was either satisfied with my response, or simply too uncomfortable to press it further.

I began to further compartmentalize both my activities and my feelings, sticking to safe topics at home—like school and my extracurricular activities. I was on the yearbook staff, participated in Youth Forum (a traveling panel of high school students sponsored by *The Dayton Daily News*), played in band, was part of Girls' State, and took roles in two serious school plays directed by a brilliant and quirky English teacher named Doug Sarff.

Sarff was probably in his mid-30s, balding and awkward, with a ski-slope nose. Even for Yellow Springs with its intellectuals and eccentrics, Sarff was an outlier, a challenging and acerbic personality, and certainly the most entertaining and uncompromising teacher I'd experienced up to that time. He'd dissect student essays openly without naming the author, but we often knew by the look on the person's face. He would write both curt critiques (*Trite! Redundant!*) and extensive comments in the margins of our papers (*Oh, god, no!*). Then, when we improved, he'd congratulate us (*Yes! That's it!*).

My junior year, we put on *Macbeth*. I desperately wanted to be Lady Macbeth, but that part went to my friend Michele Colbert. I played one of the three witches. During rehearsals, Sarff would prance around the stage, repeating our lines and exhorting us to fully engage in both the action and the deeper meaning of the work. Sometimes he would get so carried away that he'd start to lose the bridge in his mouth, and he'd cram it back in with a mumbled "goddamnit" and continue emoting.

Mr. Sarff taught English to my class for both our junior and senior years and remains a legend among my classmates. Senior year, he directed us in *Hamlet*—a play which, as we learned later, moved him profoundly.

At our most recent class reunion, a group of us began reminiscing about Doug Sarff. Someone brought up the full-page essay he had paid to publish in a Minnesota newspaper before coming to teach in Yellow Springs. He wrote: *My topic is what is rotten, not in Denmark, but in the public high school of this community; not the madness of Hamlet who was in a corrupt court from which there was no escape—but of myself who for five years taught in a spiritual slough of mediocrity...from which, fortunately, there is [escape]."*

For some of the people in my class, it was the first time they'd heard of that essay. But even five decades later, we all took pride in the fact that Sarff had never indicted Yellow Springs for the sin of mediocrity.

If the Yellow Springs School Superintendent who hired Mr. Sarff knew about the essay, he certainly could have anticipated he'd be a boat-rocker. There were rumors at the high school during those years there that Sarff was inappropriately close to some of the students he most intensely mentored. But to me, he was honest, provocative, and remarkable. And more than half a century later, I attribute my scholarship to my mom, my love of literature to Hank, and my inspiration to become a good writer to Doug Sarff.

I graduated from Yellow Springs High School in May 1969, second in my class—outranked, by Richard Hope, an arrogant teenage right-winger. I had been accepted at the four colleges where I'd applied. Having no specific academic or career aspirations, my choice among them was more driven by the absence of negatives than any particular pull. Antioch was one choice and—mostly because of the students I already knew there—seemed like a path to political activism. But, despite these new friendships and its work/study program, that choice would have tethered me to Yellow Springs and a home life rife with emotional tension and unacknowledged conflicts.

The University of New Mexico was another, and I had fond recollections of the campus with its Southwestern architecture and cultures. But Albuquerque felt like a lonely choice. I had left there as a child and seven years later had neither family nor any independent relationships to return to. Third was the honors program at the University of Michigan, but Michigan's size overwhelmed me.

And last was what became my first choice, Barnard College in New York City. Barnard is the "sister school" of Columbia University, which Hank had attended, and which he and my mom felt would provide me with an unparalleled cultural and academic environment. When I received the fat envelope containing Barnard's acceptance letter, I was thrilled—mostly, I realized later, because it made my parents happy and because I now had an answer to the question *What's next?* New York City! I really had no idea what I was doing.

Chapter Twelve

BARNARD GIRL

I entered Barnard in September 1969 when I was seventeen years old. Hank and Julia drove me to New York in the VW bus.

The summer before Barnard, I'd broken up with Prentiss and started going out with an Antioch student named Alan whom I'd met while waiting tables at the Inn. We made lukewarm promises to stay together, whatever that meant at the time, given that I'd be in New York, and Alan was thinking about transferring to the University of Maryland for money reasons. More to the point, neither of us believed we were grown-up enough to sustain a permanent relationship.

My first day at Barnard, I met my new roommate, whom I'll call M. A photo taken by Hank shows me with long brown hair, dressed in a loose purple shirt I'd made myself, bell-bottom jeans, and clogs. M was wearing a puffed sleeve, flowered dress that fell just below her knees. Her hair was done in a flip, a style I hadn't seen since Kentucky. Meeting M confirmed the trepidation I'd felt when reading the letter she'd sent during the summer, describing herself as having "hair as red as a fire truck" and "as many freckles as the sky has stars." Mr. Sarff would have had a field day with that letter.

During the summers we had spent in Dobbs Ferry, I'd visited New York City with my family a few times. I wasn't nervous, but that doesn't mean I was prepared for all eventualities. Within a few days of arriving in the city, I decided to go and visit some Antioch friends who were living in lower Manhattan, easily reachable by subway.

Every subway station had its own layout and even its own culture, and in the 116th Street #1 train station everyone stayed by the stairs near the news stand at the north end of the platform. The front area for the downtown trains and the rear area for the uptown trains were deserted. Holding a book in my hand, I descended into the station, and—for no particular reason—proceeded to walk south along the concrete platform.

In the dimly lit station, I spotted strange movements across three sets of tracks. Forty feet away, as my eyes adjusted, I could see that the movements came from a man who was masturbating, with his pants down around his knees. *Nobody is going to believe me if I tell them this story*, I thought. It was just too trite, too contrived: small-town girl's first subway trip on her own in New York City, and some idiot decides to jerk off in front of her.

Back at the dorm, over the next few days, I understood why Barnard had paired M and me. In a school where at least half the student body was from the east coast, and mostly from large suburban school districts, we were two small-town non-Jewish girls—M from a village outside Buffalo, NY, and me from southern Ohio. We both liked to sew and played in the school band.

Our similarities ended there. My parents were leftists, both English professors. M's dad worked in a factory, and her mom stayed home with the kids. Moreover, M called Black people "negroes" or "colored," the latter in reference to the girls on an adjacent floor that had been set aside for

Black students. My experiences at Antioch meant I was relatively in-the-know when it came to late-1960s campus race relations. But I certainly didn't want the responsibility of bringing M up to speed.

Just a year earlier, Barnard had made national news for expelling a student when they found out she was living unmarried with a man off-campus. With the sexual and political revolutions in full swing, encompassing protests against the Vietnam War, and systemic racism at home—students from Barnard and Columbia revolted against racism, against the war, and against rules that infringed on their personal autonomy and reflected hypocritical and long-outmoded values. The riots that took place on the Columbia campus made it clear that students wanted a voice in how the university was governed.

Now the pendulum had swung all the way in the opposite direction, and Barnard girls who formerly had to entertain male guests in the "beau parlors" on the first floor of the adjoined three dorms on campus could now invite boys to their rooms. As a consequence, there was a lot of sex (not to mention boys in the shared bathrooms) on 7 Reid, my floor in the newest dorm for first year students, located on the corner of 116th Street and Broadway.

M had a Puerto Rican boyfriend from Brooklyn whom she'd met when he'd attended an upstate program for disadvantaged NYC kids. That first week, I returned to our room more than once to find the door locked. From the hallway I could hear moaning and gasping inside. Within a couple of weeks, as Barnard precipitously liberalized its policies, the boyfriend was spending the night with M on the lower bunk in our dorm room. Though the changes overall signified honest acknowledgement that Barnard "girls" were, indeed, autonomous women, the situation with M and her boyfriend greatly inconvenienced me.

My own quasi-boyfriend was a few hundred miles away, but sex was on everyone's mind. Because I was happy to share my relative sophistication (though pretty limited experience) in those areas, my fellow classmates sometimes sought out my opinions. One of these times occurred after M and another girl from down the hall couldn't agree about the answer to the following: *Does having anal sex mean you're no longer a virgin?* I had never given the subject any thought. But I do recall thinking the question was very funny.

Finally, I couldn't take the locked door, the boyfriend in the bottom bunk, and the disparities in M's and my world views. I knew she looked up to me, but—aside from being willing to answer a question or two—I felt burdened by her. After a few weeks, I asked to be switched to another room and, by the end of my first semester at Barnard, I had a single, which suited me much better.

My classes were all right. Most of them I could reach through the underground tunnels on campus, which meant that on many winter days I could get out of bed at 8:20, throw on jeans and my favorite orange T-shirt, cruise through the dining hall and grab a hard-boiled egg or a bowl of Wheatena, and be seated in Geology (my science elective) by 9 a.m. I had plenty of time later in the day to walk around the campus, the neighborhood, and the city, and to study.

One evening something happened that took me right back to the night I was slugged at the Antioch Inn. A group of Black Barnard girls from the floor adjacent to 7 Reid had claimed a large round table in the corner of the dormitory dining hall. I was seated at a table nearby with another group of girls (all white), and one of them, Rachel (not her real name), started looking around for a saltshaker. When she saw one on the neighboring table, she went to retrieve it, saying perfunctorily, "Can I borrow the salt?" as she grabbed it and headed back to her seat. I broke into a cold sweat.

After a moment, I could see that a student from that table was asking around for the salt, and I could see another girl pointing toward Rachel. With that, the Black girl swaggered over to our table, stood in front of Rachel, and demanded: "Put the salt back."

Rachel had grown up in an all-white Long Island suburb and was clueless. "Here, you can take it," she said, holding out the saltshaker.

"Put it back," said the girl, whose name was Karen.

"Here, just take it," said Rachel.

"I said, PUT IT BACK." With that, Karen grabbed Rachel by the shirt, pulling her out of her chair and yelling and cursing at her. By now, everyone in the dining hall was watching.

A male Jamaican security guard was standing nearby, and Rachel, who was growing more hysterical by the second, pleaded with him, "Please make her take her hands off me."

I'm sure those guards were under the strictest orders to never touch a student, and he did not. Someone must have called Phyllis, the counselor-in-residence who lived with her husband in an apartment within the dorm complex. Phyllis showed up, and the moment passed somehow.

Though I enjoyed my classes at Barnard, by the end of my first year in June 1970, I felt lost, unfocused, and confused. *Why was I there?*

My favorite classes were elementary Italian and Geology, the latter taught by a wonderful professor named John Sanders. I'd written my second-semester term paper about earth creation myths among native cultures, harking back to my fifth grade Navajo sand-painting project in Albuquerque. But when I told my mother I thought I might choose Geology as a major, she discouraged me, saying, "Honey, I don't think that's a good idea. You're much stronger in the humanities."

Of course, there was no way she could have known this. My parents' cluelessness about (or even fear of) the sciences influenced me to the point that I'd avoided high school chemistry and physics, thinking they would be too difficult for me, when—for a student of my caliber—both would have been manageable and stimulating. Nevertheless, I dropped the idea of majoring in Geology. Okay, but now what?

The best part about my first year at Barnard was the New York City music and arts scene. The same Rachel of the saltshaker incident knew the ropes about getting deeply discounted student tickets to the New York City Ballet and Carnegie Hall. We'd take the subway from 116th Street to Lincoln Center or Columbus Circle, see a wonderful performance, and then walk the fifty or sixty blocks back uptown after the event. I'd played the flute throughout high school and had more than a passing familiarity with music of many genres. But this was the first time in my life I'd been able to take in live classical music performances, practically at will.

As much as I enjoyed those experiences, though, I felt disconnected, like I was an observer, longing for something I couldn't really identify. Longing for some place that was beyond my reach. And longing for love and comfort that I'd been taught, overtly or subtly, was unrealistic, if not self-indulgent. But where to go? I wondered whether I'd be better off back in Ohio. My relationship with Hank, and consequently with my mother, had been rocky through my high school years, but I missed my sister and especially my little brothers who were just seven and four when I left home.

During my visits back to Yellow Springs, I saw worrisome signs in my brother Chip. He would wake in the middle of the night cursing and crying out. When I brought it up to my mother, she said, "Chip is fine." Case closed. This pattern would persist for years—my identifying what I believed were obvious signs of trouble in the family and suggesting that maybe some kind of counseling was in order, and my mother telling me that we were all happy. By the time Chip was nine or ten, her response became, "He's just going through an early adolescence." I believe my mom's defensiveness, in part, came from a fear of offending Hank, because Chip was the only one of us four who was his biological son. Unfortunately, many of the things that worried me in my little brother manifested as grave problems in the future.

In addition, the Kent State massacre—the killing of four students and wounding of nine more by the Ohio National Guard during an anti-Vietnam War demonstration on that campus—made me both nervous and restless. I remember that May day after the killings, walking stunned across the Barnard campus and hearing someone call my name. It was the college's president, Martha Peterson, addressing me, an eighteen-year-old girl from Ohio.

"Georganne," she said, "It's terrible what's going on in your state! I hope everyone you know is safe." They were, and I truly appreciated that President Peterson had taken the time to single me out. But I was lost; I did not feel okay.

So, at the end of my freshman year, I asked Barnard to grant me a year's leave of absence. At that time, taking a break from college was not a radical thing to do. Lots of students were off, working, travelling, and planning to return to college after they "found themselves," or found something else, in the interim.

Initially, I went home to Yellow Springs, where I got a job at the local credit union. Shortly after arriving back in town, my still-sort-of boyfriend Alan (finally preparing to transfer to the University of Maryland) told me he wanted to introduce me to his best friend Jessie, a fellow Antioch student. He thought we'd like each other.

And we did. Jessie and I hit it off right away. She was blonde, blue-eyed, and intense. She'd grown up in Salt Lake City, the daughter of fairly liberal parents who were just a couple of generations away from their Mormon roots. One day shortly after Alan left town, Jessie and I took some buckets I'd grabbed from my house and went to pick raspberries on the edge of Glen Helen, the forest that was home to the iron-rich spring that gave Yellow Springs its name.

As we chatted, it emerged that each of us had thought Alan was our boyfriend. I recall both of us being more amused than irate or disappointed. After all, we were children of the 1960s, and budding women's libbers. And love–though not "free"–was at least casual. Jessie went on to become a political radical and a decade later, went to medical school and became a dermatologist. Fast forward to twenty-five years after the summer we met, and I was able to offer her the job of chief medical officer for Hudson Health Plan, the not-for-profit I ran in New York's Hudson Valley. We are still friends today.

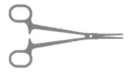

Chapter Thirteen

MUSIC AND MEN IN MAGICAL MEXICO

I n the fall of 1970, my parents arranged to spend a semester in Mexico. My mother was slated to teach at University of the Americas in Puebla, about two hours from Mexico City. I made plans to join them and flew to Mexico in February 1971.

We convened at Casa de los Amigos, a family-friendly, international hostel run by Quakers, in the center of Mexico City. Hank, my mom, my sister Julia, and my brothers Chip and Nick stayed at the hostel for a few days before going to Puebla. When I took the bus to Puebla myself, I found a small city with a charming *zócalo*, or square. But the University of the Americas was located in dusty Cholula, and it turned out that my family was living in a small house on the very dusty public highway between Puebla and Cholula.

About the only thing to do in Cholula was to visit the public market, full of barefoot American students wearing the white cotton pants and shirts of Mexican rural laborers. This appropriation of peasant attire by affluent Americans deeply offended the locals, many of whom could not afford shoes for themselves or their children. There was nothing for me there. After a week or two in Cholula, I returned to Mexico City, where Fermín, one of the gay (I realized in retrospect) Mexican men who hung out at Casa de los Amigos told me about a room for rent in the building where he lived. I went to see the room—on the *azotea* (rooftop) of a five-story walk-up in a quiet, mixed residential-commercial neighborhood a couple of blocks from Paseo de la Reforma. Just a few blocks from the Museum of Anthropology, that "penthouse" was my home base in Mexico City until my tourist visa expired six months later.

I met a man named Miguel, who worked at Casa de los Amigos, and he was my boyfriend for the first three of four months of my stay. House rules didn't allow any cohabitation except among married couples, but we managed to spend a few nights together there before I found my own place. Miguel made a point of telling me he was circumcised. Not knowing at the time that circumcision was uncommon outside the United States, I wondered out loud why that was remarkable. Miguel said he was alone among his peers in having had his foreskin removed. If he told me why that had happened to him, I don't remember.

Miguel introduced me to his best friend Jorge, who also was Mexican, and Jorge's wife Lidia, who came from Uruguay. Their beautiful, brown three-year-old son Jorgito was the first male child I saw with an intact penis. After Miguel and I broke up, the men I dated were from countries other than the United States—and all were intact. My sample size wasn't statistically significant, but that's when I began to comprehend that most of the world's men are not circumcised at birth. Though it would be a long time before I had the language and knowledge to understand the contrast in sexual intimacy between cut and uncut men, revulsion toward circumcision that began with my baby brother's experience had now taken on a new dimension.

The rooftop residents of my Rio Lerma building were an eclectic mix. Most young people in Mexico live with their families until they marry, so that meant that everyone who didn't fit that mold was unusual in some way. The only other single woman tenant leased not just one, but two adjoining rooms, including a kitchen. She let me use her refrigerator because she actually lived elsewhere with her boyfriend but kept the apartment to fool her very traditional Mexican parents. She and I shared a bathroom outside her apartment.

The building's laundry facilities were also located on the rooftop. I'd take my bar of laundry soap and my clothes to the huge cast-stone, cold-water sink with a built-in washboard, and scrub away. I never felt it was a hardship to hand-wash and hang out to dry the little clothing I owned. The building's woman manager furnished me with clean sheets every so often.

I loved living on that rooftop. I could come and go as I pleased and had enough sociability not to feel lonely. I spent a night here and there with Carlos Lupercio, a painter who went by his last name only, and who shared an apartment with an artist friend. He was lovely, but I appreciated having no obligation to keep him or anyone else posted on my activities.

Calling home to Ohio (to which my family had returned after a couple of months in Cholula) was prohibitively expensive, so I never phoned. I ate cheaply: *a licuado* (the original smoothie) in the morning and a delicious *comida corrida* (daily special) midday in one or another inexpensive restaurant. For dinner I'd eat yogurt and fruit unless somebody asked me out. Street vendors were a great source of fresh pineapple or mango sprinkled with chili powder.

My mother's cousin Kay, who had grown up in Hawaii and Athens, Greece, was married to a handsome Spaniard named Francisco Negrín. They lived with their two boys in Lomas de Zamora, a fancy neighborhood half an hour by *pesero* (public taxi) from my apartment. Kay had started La Visita, the first ready-to-wear maternity clothes company in Mexico, and her small factory was located above their garage. It was Francisco's job to take the colorful cotton dresses—inspired by Hawaiian *mu'umu'us*—to the new discount department stores around the city. People in Mexico had a lot of babies, the middle class was growing, and Kay had created a genius business.

Occasionally, she and Francisco invited me for the midday meal. Or I'd visit Lidia and her family or get together with friends from Ohio or New York who happened to be visiting. But I was on my own much of the time, wandering the then still-safe streets in both working class and charming residential neighborhoods; spending whole days in the Museum of Anthropology (which helped to shape my later decision to major in that subject); and hanging out at Casa de los Amigos where visitors came through from all over the world. Every day was exhilarating.

Having taken four years of high school Spanish, when I first arrived in Mexico City I could pretty much make myself understood. But my comprehension was terrible. People would ask me "*Hablas español?* (Do you speak Spanish?"), I would answer "*Sí,*" and then completely drown in the torrent of their next sentences. A month passed before I was able to hold a somewhat natural conversation in the language, and I would go to bed every night exhausted by the effort. By the time I left six months later, though, I was dreaming in Spanish, and I've been comfortable in that language ever since.

In Mexico City, in addition to discovering the male foreskin, I became enamored of South American folk music. During the early 1970s, as right-wing authoritarian regimes were rising up in Chile and Argentina, those governments and paramilitary organizations began targeting artists, intellectuals, teachers, social workers—anyone who might view poor people with compassion and speak out (or sing out) out about their plight. Middle-class, educated South Americans with the means to leave started emigrating, some to Europe, and a good number to Mexico.

My friend Julio, a Mexican engineer, introduced me to Claudio and Marina, an Argentine couple. Claudio and Marina, in turn, introduced me to other South American expatriate musicians who wrote protest music and performed on traditional folk instruments, and to a handful of Mexicans who were also immersed in that genre.

I'd played the transverse (horizontally held) flute since fifth grade and was adept at playing by ear as well as improvising. Claudio and Marina gifted me a *quena* (or kena), a bamboo flute (held vertically) that became my preferred instrument for the next twenty years. The music I fell in love with was similar to American protest music, with its poignant lyrics about injustice, poverty, love (romantic love and love for the homeland)... and loss. A lot about loss. Unlike my South American companions, I could safely return to my country, but I deeply related to their exile. I'd gradually come to feel like more and more of an outsider in my own family—rootless, with no real place that I could settle into and call home. Their stories and the music spoke to me then, and still do.

In the summer of 1971, a few weeks before my visa expired, I fell for a charming man named Luigi, Italian by birth but raised in Mexico City. Luigi worked for Olivetti, the typewriter company. We met at an office supply trade show where I had been hired (off the books, of course) to wear a short skirt and staff a product booth. We spent a passionate weekend in Valle del Bravo, a colonial mountain town west of Mexico City, and he asked me to come back to live with him after I obtained a new visa and could return legally. My pseudo-empowered twenty-year-old self was careful to tell Luigi that I didn't want to cook and clean, and he assured me he didn't expect that. "I have no intentions of making you into a housewife," he said.

I informed Barnard (and my very annoyed mother) that I wanted another semester off, believing I'd buy time and figure things out. Luigi took me to the airport, and I must have badly wanted not to leave, because it was the only occasion in my life that I nearly missed my flight despite being in the boarding lounge.

Before returning to Ohio, I flew through Los Angeles to Honolulu, where I visited my Tutu. Back in Yellow Springs a few weeks later, I was able to go back to my old job at the credit union, and part-time weekend shifts at the Antioch Inn.

I was desperate to hear Luigi's voice, but his promised calls were few and far between. One day, I dialed the home number he'd given me, and a maid answered the phone. "Mr. Milanesi doesn't live here," she told me. "He lives in another place, with his wife and baby."

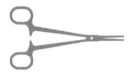

Chapter Fourteen

BARNARD REDUX, ANTHROPOLOGY, AND SOUTH AMERICAN MUSIC

I can't say I was devastated—more chagrined at my naiveté. Perhaps I knew deep down that my plan to return to Mexico, where I couldn't work legally, where I barely knew the man with whom I'd promised to live, was impractical at best. Either way, I needed a new plan, something less fantastical.

During that time in Yellow Springs, I was hanging out with new and old friends, including a close high school companion, musician, and sometimes lover named Duane Schumacher. Duane lived in a tiny loft next to his mother's house in the commune-like Vale, on the outskirts of Yellow Springs. One morning I appeared at home after spending the night at Duane's. My mother, increasingly exasperated with me not being in school, confronted me about "shacking up" with him. In a voice dripping with sarcasm, she asked, "Why don't you just get *MARRIED*?" I see now that she must have been reliving her own history—leaving college to marry my birth father, which did not work out well for her.

Shortly after that, she gave me an ultimatum: "Go back to Barnard, or it won't be an option anymore." This meant I'd have to choose a cheaper school, because Julia was going to be graduating from high school soon and there wouldn't be enough money to pay for two tuitions. My options then would be Ohio State or Wilmington College where, by then, both of my parents were on the faculty and which I could attend tuition-free.

Neither would have been a bad choice, but by that time I'd started to form some aspirations for my academic future. My time in Mexico had awakened in me an interest in anthropology—from my childhood in Hawaii, to my interest in other cultures and languages, from my exposure to the complexities of race and class during my three years in Kentucky, from both the openly acknowledged and the buried tensions underlying my own family constellation, and my growing understanding of power dynamics and social injustice issues as I came of age in Yellow Springs. From all of this, I believed that anthropology might be a key to me gaining a better understanding of the world and my place in it.

I knew that both Barnard College and its affiliate Columbia University had stellar departments in that discipline. Also, after being relatively oblivious to such things, I'd begun to appreciate that a Barnard degree carried a good deal of prestige. I had enjoyed my break but didn't want to waste an opportunity that would carry me forward into a career I could love, whatever that might be.

I went back to New York and took a job during the Christmas season working in the pet accessories department of B. Altman, the high-end department store on 5th Avenue and 34th Street. The very kind parents of an Antioch friend offered to let me stay in their apartment in the West Village for the month of December before I moved back into a Barnard dorm. Barbara, my friend's mother, was a psychotherapist, and informally counseled me about some of the confusion and distress I was feeling and witnessing with regard to my family. One night we were talking, and Barbara expressed shock when she realized that "my father" was actually my mother's second husband, who had come into my life when I was eight years old. She said, "You were a fully formed person when he married your mother. It's natural that you would see each other more as competition for your mother's attention than as father and daughter." The interesting thing was that she said it so matter-of-factly. Barbara's words would return to me over and over in the future, helping me to understand myself, Hank, my mother's perpetual balancing act, and our family interrelationships. I felt enormous gratitude for her and her husband's generosity with their home, and the emotional support they provided at a time when I was struggling to find myself. Over the years, I have tried to help other young people with a sympathetic ear and a place to stay when they couldn't find that support at home.

In early January, I re-entered Barnard. Unlike during my first year, this time I had a purpose. I was going to become an anthropologist.

In the eighteen months I'd been away, friends from freshman year had moved off-campus. No matter. Dormitory living (in a single room, of course) suited me. No kitchen to clean, no excess stuff, and it was safe and comfortable.

I'd managed to retain my scholarship from Barnard, and, between that and my parents' help, my tuition was covered. But I needed to earn my own spending money, so I took a job in the cataloguing department at Columbia's Butler Library. The pay was terrible, $2.25 an hour, but I made a few new friends my age who were not students. Then someone told me that Zabar's, a fancy delicatessen on Broadway and West 80th Street, was hiring and that they paid real money. I landed the job after a brief interview with Murray Klein, the managing partner, and immediately started scooping coffee beans into one-pound bags (Zabar's sold dozens of varieties long before coffee became a thing). Shortly after, I graduated to the cheese section and, to this day, I can estimate the weight of a block of cheese or a bag of coffee within a fraction of an ounce.

Soon I was making nearly double what the library had paid and, simultaneously, was treated to an extracurricular anthropology course in NYC's Upper West Side, liberal, Jewish culture. Just as Georgetown, Kentucky and Yellow Springs, Ohio, helped me to understand racial politics, my experience at Zabar's would prove exceedingly helpful in navigating the religious politics of circumcision when I became involved in the intactivist movement nearly thirty years later.

My Zabar's schedule was Friday noon to 10 p.m., Saturday noon to midnight, and Sunday 10 to 6 p.m. The dorm cafeteria didn't provide weekend meals, but thanks to the Zabar brothers and Murray Klein, all who realized that the cost of feeding employees was insignificant compared to the benefits of having them on the sales floor, we were able to help ourselves to pretty much anything in the store. Two rules: the beluga caviar was off limits, and anything we took had to be consumed on premises during our breaks. My particular favorites were the fresh lobster salad from the deli and the dense whole grain rolls from the bakery section. I remembered my mother telling me how her Greek restaurant-owning family had a similar philosophy, bolstered with a practicality that no doubt was shared by the Jewish owners of Zabar's: let your employees eat whatever they want, because the cost of the food is a small price to pay for good will and loyal workers. This was another Zabar's freebie—management dos-and-don'ts that would pay off in my future executive career. On top of all that, I now could afford to buy my own plane tickets home to Ohio, and even sprang for a couple of weeks in Mexico over Christmas in 1972.

Working all weekend at the busiest delicatessen in New York was exhausting. It also cut into my schoolwork. I eventually gave up the Sunday hours, to have more time to study and to sleep.

My coursework at Barnard was exhilarating. Between freshman year and a couple of summer courses I'd picked up at Wilmington College (where my parents taught) during my year-and-a-half away, by the time I re-enrolled at Barnard I had completed most of my basic requirements. This allowed me to focus on my declared major and take courses in other departments that built upon my growing fascination with anthropology and the way it conceptualized the world. As a small undergraduate institution that prided itself on its excellent teaching, Barnard offered a high-quality, highly engaged faculty. And most of my fellow students were equally engaged in learning.

I tested out of my language requirement (Spanish), and enrolled in elementary French, which came easily to me. This enabled me to take advanced literature courses in both languages, further allowing me windows into other cultures through literature written in their authors' native tongues. The most memorable was Negritude, taught by a beyond-brilliant professor named Serge Gavronsky. The course focused on literature from French colonies in Africa and the Caribbean. We read *Les Damnés de la Terre (The Wretched of the Earth)*, by Martinican psychiatrist and revolutionary Frantz Fanon, the poetry of Aimé Cesaire (also from Martinique), and other works dealing with the colonial experience, including human slavery and centuries of economic and cultural repression. All of these themes only deepened my interest in social class and the use of race and stigma to enforce norms imposed by a dominant culture.

Later, all of this would resonate with me as I began to learn the history of circumcision in the United States and how, in addition to Victorian morality, racism played an enormous part.

With my classmates and teachers, we also pondered how social change occurs, and how the participant observation method of anthropology offered opportunities for bringing about positive change.

Chapter Fifteen
ON MY OWN

The fall of my senior year at Barnard, as I descended the stairs into a midtown subway station, I spotted a guy with a big black beard playing an Irish tin whistle. He was surrounded by an array of folk instruments—mostly flutes—spread on a blanket on a large landing. We introduced ourselves (his name was Bill Ochs) and began chatting about music. When I mentioned that I'd become involved with Andean and South American folk music during a long stay in Mexico and that I played the kena, Bill said he'd like to introduce me to his Peruvian friend Guillermo, who was seeking musicians for an Andean music group. A few days later, Guillermo called me. Soon after, he recruited a Bolivian *bombo* (folk drum) player and we began to perform as Tahuantinsuyo, the first Andean music group in New York City.[6]

During my last year in college, Tahuantinsuyo performed in public and private venues throughout the city. We must have played "El Condor Pasa" (the song Simon and Garfunkel popularized as "If I Could" or – more popularly – "I'd rather be a hammer than a nail...") a thousand times. The core was Guillermo and me, with other musicians standing in on occasion. At one point, two sisters from northern Mexico joined us. One was a Barnard student and the other attended Manhattan School of Music, also in the Columbia neighborhood. My favorite place to play was a coffee house called Café Latinoamericano, on 55th Street between 5th and 6th Avenues. I liked it because it was small, and because no liquor was served so the crowd came not to drink, but because they wanted to hear the music.

I look back now and have a hard time comprehending how I managed all my activities and obligations. I was taking a heavier than average course load so I could graduate in seven rather than eight semesters and playing music three or four nights a week. During my senior year, I'd enrolled in a graduate level course taught by an anthropologist named Lambros Comitas. Greek American and the same age as my mother, Lambros quickly became a mentor. He had done fieldwork and conducted research projects throughout the West Indies and consulted on a Peace Corps project in Bolivia. He was warm, compassionate, smart, and very funny. Students loved him, he was widely respected by his contemporaries, and he seemed to make friends and lasting relationships wherever he went.

I gave up my job at Zabar's when Lambros offered me a job overseeing the production of the second edition of *Caribbeana*, a multi-volume subject-indexed bibliography of Caribbean literature. It was a massive project—the kind that ultimately went by the wayside with the advent of digital research and printing. We worked out of the Research Institute for the Study of Man (RISM) on East 78th Street in Manhattan, a private anthropological research organization founded by a wealthy anthropologist named Vera Rubin.

The Caribbean literature I reviewed as part of my job further deepened my interest in the history of race, slavery, and social class in the Americas. For my senior thesis, I used an anthropological theory called structuralism to analyze how humans and cultures categorize people or phenomena in a binary way (homosexual versus heterosexual; Black versus white; slave versus free; impure versus pure; us versus them). Such categorization results in both stigmatization and appallingly inhumane behavior toward individuals or groups being negatively characterized. The body of knowledge and insights I gained in my study of anthropology continue to this day to inform my analysis of genital cutting (circumcised versus "uncircumcised") and the stigma associated with the male foreskin in American culture today.

Anthropologist Margaret Mead spoke at Commencement when I graduated from Barnard in 1974. My mom was in Honolulu taking care of Tutu, but my Grandma Jean (Hank's mother) came to the ceremony. Just before I was to move out of the Barnard dorm and into an apartment whose lease was held by Rebecca, the daughter of a Columbia Journalism professor on 114th Street. Jackie, the girl whose room I was to supposed to take over told me she wasn't ready to leave, and that I'd have to figure out something else for a month or two. I truly don't remember where I stashed my meager belongings, but I slept on different friends' couches for a few weeks. In addition to the discomfort of moving from place to place, I felt embarrassed about not having a place of my own or any family nearby to rely upon. More than once, I ended up spending the night with a guy out of convenience, rather than any desire for his companionship. Eventually, I moved into "Jackie's room" in Rebecca's 114th Street apartment.

Despite having graduated from Barnard *magna cum laude* and Phi Beta Kappa, despite close friends and the confidence of my academic and professional mentor, I felt like the girl Bob Dylan called out in his ballad: "How does it feel to be on your own, with no direction home, like a complete unknown, like a rolling stone?"

At RISM, I had hired and was responsible for supervising two other women around my age. We spent hours and days at a time in the RISM library, as well as the main branch of the New York Public Library on 42nd Street, poring over articles and books, and manually classifying and indexing them. At the age of 22, I had no training or skill at managing other people. My "staff" members were—essentially—my peers, and my insecurity coupled with my role as "boss" provoked minor but stressful arguments, such as whether a misspelling in the title of an article should be reproduced or corrected in the citation.

In the meantime, my job and the music kept me engaged. Tahuantinsuyo rehearsed or performed nearly every night. Along with Guillermo and me, a rotating cast of two or three other musicians made up the group. Luis, from Bolivia, played guitar and charango—a stringed instrument made from the shell of an armadillo. He was unreliable, though, mostly due to his drinking; one night he showed up without his guitar because his Dominican wife had smashed it into a thousand pieces. Jorge, an Argentine Jew, struggled to play the *bombo* (the Andean drum). Once Ecuadorian architect and excellent guitarist Pepe Santana joined the group, the caliber of our performances shot up, but so did the conflicts. Pepe and Guillermo tangled over repertoire, and engaged in futile disagreements about whether our music was truly indigenous, truly "authentic." Tahuantinsuyo was like a multi-party marriage with exponential tensions.

Late that summer, we began to look in earnest for a new band member—someone who could sing (none of us had much of a voice), play the guitar, and expand our repertoire. One night, a guy named Eduardo showed up at a rehearsal. We had friends in common, and someone had told him to check us out. It was clear from the moment he arrived that he had the talent we were looking for—a wonderful tenor voice, and proficiency on both the guitar and *bombo*. Blond with green eyes, he also happened to be very handsome. After a couple of rehearsals, though, he stopped coming. He sent word that his father in Argentina had died, and that he had to take care of some business but would be back.

Around Thanksgiving, Eduardo called me. He told me he'd taken a temporary part-time job so he could send money back to Argentina. He asked if there was still a place for him in Tahuantinsuyo. I was pretty sure the answer was yes, so I invited him to the next rehearsal where he was accepted into the group. And after a few weeks, we were a couple, spending almost every night together whether we were rehearsing, performing, or just hanging out in my rented room on 114th Street.

When Eduardo became a part of Tahuantinsuyo, our repertoire exploded. Before that, most of the songs we played were instrumental only and came from an Andean tradition. Argentine folk music, on the other hand, was heavily poetic and lyrical. There were songs about nostalgia for home and family, about injustice and tragedy, about love and loss, even about faithful dogs and horses. I was hooked, falling in love with both the man and the stories he was bringing to my life—stories that resonated with my own experience, and of course his, too. I told my mother about Eduardo and about the music, but without much detail. There was no way I could explain to her the intense emotions I was feeling. And she didn't pursue the conversation. I was in New York, and she had her own pressures.

Around the same time I met Eduardo, my family moved from Yellow Springs and the house we'd lived in when I was in high school. Mom and Hank had built a new house in Wilmington, Ohio, near the Quaker college where they both taught. The Wilmington house was designed around a small open-air atrium, something that meant a lot to Hank. Unfortunately, the cost and design constraints of the atrium compromised both the size and comfort of the rest of the house. It had three normal-sized bedrooms—one for my parents, and one for each of my brothers. The tiny guest room, which was supposed to accommodate Julia and me, barely held a full-size bed, let alone any other furnishings. There was literally no room for me to stay for more than a night or two.

Hank told me I needed to remove my belongings because there wouldn't be any space to store them in the new house. The complication, of course, was that I didn't have a place of my own—only a rented room in an apartment where someone else held the lease. I consolidated photos, mementos, a few items of clothing, and my high school yearbooks into a small, old-time steamer trunk and somehow got it to New York City. That trunk would stay with me for another 30 years.

For me, the Wilmington house signaled definitively that I no longer belonged in the family that had been my security—albeit often strained—since I was eight. Now, the new family would be my mom, Hank, Chip, and Nick.

If confirmation of that fact was needed, I discovered that just before the move to Wilmington, my parents and my brothers had been filmed and interviewed for a television documentary about interracial adoption. For reasons I never understood, neither Julia nor I were included or even mentioned in the film. Years later, I brought up the subject to my mother, telling her how confused and hurt I felt when I found I'd been excluded. She didn't deny it had happened and gave me an infuriating non-answer:

"It was a long time ago," it served no purpose to talk about it now, and I should get over my resentment.

Later, when I became involved in the intactivist movement, I began to hear from circumcision survivors whose parents or other loved ones refused to acknowledge their pain or answer their questions. Some of those stories would remind me of my feelings when I found out about that documentary and tried to talk about it with my mother. Without a doubt, this experience shaped my ability to relate to and empathize with people whose need to understand *what happened and why* is dismissed by those who were supposed to protect and advocate for them. A parent's defense that a child should forget a traumatic event because it happened long ago, or because the parent wanted to put it behind them, misses the point. The child was hurt and needs at least to be heard, if not comforted with an apology.

Reliving all of this with the benefit of hindsight, I realize how little emotional support I had from my family at times I truly needed it. I internalized my mother's deflection of my feelings about being rejected as a message that I should—and could—stand on my own two feet and make my own decisions. Had I felt more cared for, I probably would not have ended up marrying Eduardo when I was just 23.

Chapter Sixteen

MARRYING AND MAKING BEAUTIFUL MUSIC

When I told my mother a few months later that Eduardo and I were thinking about marriage, she was kind and thoughtful, and she cautioned me against it. She knew he'd only recently arrived in New York from Argentina and that he had little formal education. She wasn't a snob. But she also knew that no matter how much the music bound us together, the class differences between Eduardo and me would likely increase, rather than dissipate, over time. Hank made a similar point, not so much about education directly, but about its implications for our respective income. They were right. But I didn't listen because I was on my own.

And something more. Over the years, I've realized that although Eduardo was more obviously uprooted from his family and culture, I also had no family to return to. We were two young people, lost in New York City. And we both needed a home.

On May 2, 1975, we took the subway downtown and said our marital vows. I'd sewn a blue cotton dress with tiny flowers for the occasion, but it was a cold day, so I donned a mauve skirt with a new long-sleeved t-shirt. Eduardo wore a red Argentine poncho over his khakis and dress shirt. A photo taken outside City Hall shows us flanked by our witnesses—two musician friends and John Birmingham, Rebecca's very tall, blond boy-friend. We look happy. I was touched to have my sister Julia there as well; she surprised me by appearing in New York the night before, saying "I figured I ought to at least be present for your first marriage."

Music was both the bond and lifestyle that carried Eduardo and me through the first few years as a married couple. Eduardo was hand-some and sexy and talented, with a fantastic tenor voice. Our mutual attraction and musical compatibility shone on stage, and we became minor stars in a small circle of South American folk music followers. We hung out with other folk musicians, all but me from South America. We rehearsed on weekdays. Then on Friday and Saturday nights, we'd play at a coffee house in midtown Manhattan, followed by a gig at one or another Argentine restaurant in Queens. At that point, other musi-cians—some of them extraordinary—would join in and we'd end up jamming together in someone's apartment after the restaurant shut its doors. Around daybreak, we'd hit an all-night diner before going home to sleep until afternoon. It was exhausting and wonderful. The hundred or so dollars we'd make in a night more than covered the cost of gas, gui-tar strings, and breakfast.

I didn't take Eduardo's last name—never even considered it. I had already changed my name once, when my mother married Hank, and had no desire to repeat that experience. Perhaps because it is common in Latin American countries for women to retain their father's name after marriage, we never discussed a name change. Later, I realized we had spent very little time discussing anything but music, neglecting issues related to male/female roles, personality quirks, domestic preferences, children, my professional goals, travel, family. Signs of trouble in my marriage were there from the start, mostly sparked by Eduardo's extreme jealousy, suspicion, and the fact that he was both unfamiliar with and threatened by what was normal behavior for my American female peers. The same things that appealed to Eduardo about me—my independence, gregariousness, and openness to other cultures and people— simultaneously terrified him.

My answer to the questions people often asked, "Why do you speak Spanish so well?" and "How did you learn about our music?" included the fact that I'd lived in Mexico City for several months when I was twenty years old and had been playing with a group of South American expatriates. I somehow missed that in Eduardo's mind, an American woman traveling alone in Latin America could only be doing one thing—whoring around.

He repressed the thought some of the time, but it surfaced all too often, and I became wary of talking openly in front of him.

I'd begun a graduate program in anthropology at Columbia. Less than a month after our wedding day, I'd be traveling to Bolivia for my first fieldwork experience, which meant a three-month separation from my new husband. Now as I analyze Eduardo's apparent acceptance of my plan to work and live in Bolivia for three months and pursue a career that would demand many more long separations like that, I realize that my new husband realized the Bolivia trip was non-negotiable, but figured we could start over on his terms when I returned.

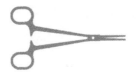

Chapter Seventeen

FROM BOLIVIA TO MY REAL LIFE

The three months I spent in rural Bolivia in 1975 showed me two things. One, I didn't have the self-discipline to do what was required to become an anthropologist. I couldn't spend my days watching people and documenting everything they were doing and saying, and this ethnographic approach was still the core of anthropology fieldwork, prerequisite to a PhD.

The second thing it showed me was malnutrition and disease. Of course, I had known that people who were poor struggled to pay for food. And I knew at that point that health care was a privilege and not a right in the United States. But I'd never seen rampant, obvious malnutrition. In the home I grew up in, "not having money" was a relative and not an absolute term; and nobody (so far as I knew) in my relatively healthy family had suffered from lack of medical care. Because of all this, I had absolutely no idea what real hunger, real poverty, and intractable illness looked like.

In the village of Mururata—only 100 kilometers from Bolivia's largest city La Paz—I saw sweet, Black and indigenous children with big eyes and big bellies, but legs and arms so skinny you could see their bones. I saw two-year-old babies who still couldn't walk. I saw handsome

Angel, the Afro-Bolivian mayor, standing outside his house every morning, coughing up blood into a handkerchief—almost certainly because of tuberculosis, which was endemic in the region. I watched the wedding procession of Julia and Felix, as their four-year-old son Roberto trailed behind them with his milky eyes and crooked legs.

It wasn't until I left anthropology and enrolled in a joint program between Columbia's School of Arts and Sciences and the School of Public Health that I began to put things together. I took a class in tropical diseases and was able to understand in retrospect some of what I had seen in the subtropical Bolivian Yungas. I began to acquire the tools to analyze what I'd already intuitively known—and that still eludes too many of us:

* Poverty, malnutrition, and disease are inextricably linked,

* Much of "health care" doesn't address most causes of disease.

I also was beginning to realize that being able to afford medical care does not automatically benefit you but can actually make you a target for exploitation.

Unfortunately, most of the faculty members in my department (sociomedical sciences) at Columbia were focused on quantitative analysis—mining existing bodies of data trends in health status and medical care utilization. I, on the other hand, wanted to talk about disease stigma, poverty, the growing tendency of physicians and the pharmaceutical industry to over-medicalize common conditions, and the social control the medical establishment exercises over people who are vulnerable either because of their socioeconomic status or their stage in life (for example, pregnant women and babies). Though the details may have changed, these concerns still grip me today.

On the home front, my husband had no particular interest in what I was studying. He just wanted me to play music with him.

My ability to compartmentalize as a buffer against the pain I often felt in my family and now with Eduardo served me well enough in the early years of our marriage. And we did have good times. While we were singing and playing, any tensions faded into the background.

Eventually some members of Tahuantinsuyo went their own way. Eduardo and I began performing as a duo or with an occasional third person. For the next few years, we had a good following in New York's South American community and among others who followed the genre of protest music we played. We'd also begun to produce small concerts with visiting Argentine folk musicians.

After four years of marriage, though, a big problem arose. We had moved to Queens, one of New York City's outer boroughs, which was better for Eduardo's commute to the auto repair shop where he worked. It was also better for the music. Our apartment in a two-family house was large enough for us to rehearse, and the neighbors didn't seem to mind. But living in Queens meant I had a nearly two-hour commute each way to Columbia University, where I was in graduate school and also working part-time.

The solution was that Eduardo would pick me up after any evening classes. But that meant I couldn't join my fellow students for an impromptu cup of coffee, or even hang out chatting for fifteen minutes after class was over. The dividing line between my personal life and my academic and career interests was something I should have anticipated but had not.

I wanted to move back to Manhattan, where I'd been living when we first met, near to school and near to my friends. Yes, it would add another half hour each way to Eduardo's commute, but with a car travel-ing against traffic, and his regular schedule, which didn't seem to me to be so much of a burden.

Eduardo wasn't interested, though, and dug in his heels. I insisted. Of course, our fight about where in New York City to live was both practical and cultural. I wanted to be in a university neighborhood, and he was more comfortable in the immigrant working-class neighborhood where we lived in Queens. I had moved from a graduate program in anthropology to one in sociomedical sciences and was beginning to see career possibilities in international health. He couldn't imagine *what* he'd do in Jamaica, Paraguay, or Bolivia, for example, if that's where my work took me. What was really at stake was big, and I was beginning to realize it was only going to get bigger.

I decided to make a break for it. I rented a tiny Columbia apartment on Riverside Drive and broke the news the night after I'd signed the lease. "I love you, but this isn't going to work," I said. "I am leaving,"

He panicked, and immediately said he'd move.

"No, our differences are too big, and it is better to that we go our separate ways," I told him.

That's when he pulled out the one card that could change my mind. "We could have a baby."

I'd been telling him for the past couple of years that I'd like to get pregnant sooner rather than later – that it would be a good time to do that while I was in grad school, that we could afford it, and could even fit a baby into our musical life. He thought the timing wasn't right. But when he put a baby on the table, I caved.

I got pregnant on day one in the new apartment, on the couch, sur-rounded by moving boxes.

Just a couple of years into my marriage, my mother, Hank and my two brothers moved from Ohio to Hawaii. My grandmother, my Tutu, was suffering from Alzheimer's disease and my mother's sister had passed away a few years earlier, so there was no one to take care of Tutu.

This meant, as my marriage was evolving, there were 5,000 miles between me and my family. I visited Hawaii, yes, but the trip was long and expensive so I couldn't go often. And the Honolulu household was troubled, too, with not just one (my grandmother) but two mentally ill family members; my brother Chip, high school age at the time, was showing increasing signs of what would eventually be diagnosed as schizophrenia, though it took a long time for my parents to recognize how sick he was. During one of my visits to Honolulu, I was in the kitchen with my grandmother when we heard Chip stomping up the outside steps. Tutu stiffened and said, "Oh, it's that man. Now we're really in trouble." She knew something was very wrong with him but had no idea he was her grandson.

While I was pregnant, Eduardo and I decided to look for a place outside New York City. Manhattan was feeling dirty and unsafe in those days, and the rent on good-size apartments was out of our reach. Our car, which we parked on Riverside Drive just north of Columbia's International House, had been broken into several times.

My friend Rachel told us about Nyack, just twenty miles north and on the western bank of the Hudson River, less than half an hour trip by car to Columbia. One weekend we took a drive there. As we cruised into town, I saw people on bikes, barefoot hippies, an old stone building that served as the public library, a natural foods store, craft shops. It reminded me of Yellow Springs! That same day, we put in an offer on a small working-class Victorian house and proceeded to put together the $6,000 we would need to close; we would be able to move a few weeks after the baby's birth.

If I had any doubt that we were making the right move, a couple of months before Ernesto was born, a young woman who lived in our building on Riverside Drive was followed home from the grocery store. The guy shoved his way into the building behind her, forced her into the elevator, and took her to the top floor where he raped her. I couldn't get out of my head the thought (and terror) that the victim of that attack could easily have been the slow, very pregnant me.

Chapter Eighteen
BEST LAID PLANS

To the alarm of some of my academic peers, I had planned a home birth. My skepticism about the medical industry—in particular, obstetrics, with its history of drugs, episiotomies, and circumcision—inspired me to look for alternatives to a hospital delivery. Even a nice freestanding birth center seemed like too much trouble. At age 28, I was young enough, healthy enough, and educated enough about the birth process to prepare myself, I thought. *Why leave home to have a baby? Why not have a midwife come to me and give birth in my own bed?*

Eduardo supported that choice. The other thing we agreed about, confirmed in only the briefest conversation, was that if our child was a boy, nobody was going to cut his penis. "What? Are they crazy? How could anybody do that to a baby?" asked my husband rhetorically.

The two New York City nurse midwives who cared for me during my pregnancy were home birth pros. They worked with an obstetrician, who was similarly non-interventionist and who served as their back-up if a woman for any reason needed to go to the hospital to deliver her baby.

The homebirth protocol included a visit by the pregnant mom to the back-up OB during the last few weeks of pregnancy. I cannot recall the name of the doctor I met, but I do remember that he was kind and attentive. I told him that if for any reason I was unable to give birth at home, we did not want our baby circumcised. He said that was fine. Had he pushed back, I'm not sure I would have much noticed. My baby was going to be born at home, with a midwife, and my midwives were fully onboard with keeping boys whole.

My due date was Monday, September 1. August was stifling, and due to the baby's position in my womb, my right ankle was so swollen that I could barely walk. To my embarrassment, I remember getting angry at a friend who suggested that she could pick me up and we could go shopping. *How could she be so clueless?* I complained to my husband. I also was increasingly spooked about the idea of leaving our apartment, because of my neighbor's horrible experience.

Out of wishful thinking or maybe desperation, I convinced myself my baby was not just "due" (a word that denotes options or probability) but was guaranteed to appear on Labor Day. On Thursday the week before, I plopped myself down on one of the chairs at our small kitchen table and announced that from that moment on, I would move only between that chair and our bed (oh, and the bathroom). The baby was *certain* to arrive by Monday night.

Monday midday, while sitting on that kitchen chair, I felt a pop and a surge of warm liquid between my legs. Things were going according to plan! I called Scotti Formato, the midwife on call, and reported that my water had broken. She asked me to monitor my contractions—barely perceptible at that point.

Over the next few hours, nothing much happened. Scotti appeared later that night to examine me and told my husband to find me some black cohosh tea, which should help to move my labor along. All day Tuesday, I drank the tea and walked around our very small apartment. I even forced myself to go outside and hike a few steps up and down the block. By evening, I was still not showing much progress, and Scotti broke the news that if I wasn't in active labor by late that night, I would have to go to the hospital.

According to medical guidelines nurse midwives were required to follow, she explained, once a patient's water breaks and she undergoes an internal exam, infection becomes a risk. If labor doesn't progress rather quickly, a home delivery becomes riskier. She told my husband and me that we should be prepared to be at Lenox Hill hospital very early the next morning to meet the midwives' back-up obstetrician and—likely—undergo induction.

I was devastated. I felt that not being able to deliver my baby at home was a failure of will or evidence of a character defect. Another disappointment came when Scotti told me the doctor I'd seen in the last month of my pregnancy was on vacation and wouldn't be the person delivering my baby. His back-up, whom she had not met but assumed was okay, would take care of me. The back-up to the back-up; it didn't sound promising.

I remember Eduardo helping me to pack a bag, and the next morning we went by taxi to Lenox Hill Hospital on Manhattan's East Side. As we entered the lobby through the front door, whom should I see but Dr. Juan Negrín, father-in-law of my Greek-Hawaiian Mexico City cousin Kay. Dr. Negrín practiced neurosurgery at Lenox Hill, and I had met him several times when my Greek relatives visited New York from Athens. To my surprise, he recognized me immediately and greeted me warmly. It didn't take a lot of explaining for him to understand why I was lumbering through the lobby of Lenox Hill at 6 a.m. on a Wednesday, and he promised to visit me later in the day.

I was installed in the labor and delivery unit somewhere upstairs, and the back-up obstetrician arrived to introduce himself. Dr. Radoslav Jovanovic was kind and soft-spoken. I told him, first, that if the baby was a boy, I did not want him circumcised and, second, that I did not want to be drugged during the birth. He immediately agreed to my no-circumcision position, and I recall feeling he was pleased about that. His response to my second demand was more nuanced—appropriately so. He explained he would not administer any analgesics without my express permission. He also said he would accelerate labor gently, and that if I experienced pain or anxiety, he would consult with me about what, if any, pain relief I would accept. And he was true to his word.

Ernesto Santiago Echeverria emerged at 7:20 the evening of September 3. He was born with a full head of platinum blond hair, making him the envy of the newborn nursery during the few hours he wasn't rooming in with me. Soon after I settled into bed to rest for the first time in 60 hours, Dr. Negrín stopped by to say hello and wish us well.

For the rest of our stay, not a single doctor or nurse asked us about circumcision. Only over the coming decades would I realize how fortunate both Ernesto and I were in having Dr. Jovanovic attend my birth, and how utterly unusual it was to have evaded the relentless marketing of male genital cutting so common in hospitals in the United States. Thus, on Friday, September 5, we were able to take our whole baby home to the small apartment on Riverside Drive, now housing a family of three.

Chapter Nineteen
HOPSCOTCH

In early October of 1980, five weeks after Ernesto's birth, we loaded up a U-Haul and moved to our new home in Nyack.

I was still in graduate school at Columbia's uptown campus, which housed the medical center and the school of public health. Within a few weeks, I found a babysitter near that campus and began commuting to the city by public transportation. The trip involved putting my baby son into a stroller, walking to the bus, usually sitting in the back so I could nurse him during the trip, and then—on the other end—placing him back into the stroller and walking the nine blocks to Juanita's apartment, a block away from where most of my classes were held. Then, a few hours later, I did the reverse.

As I was finishing up the course requirements for my PhD, I also worked as a research assistant at the School of Public Health. Together with Giorgio Solimano, a physician/academic who had fled Chile after Salvador Allende was killed. I wrote a long paper on the effects of socio-economic development and ecological change on health and nutrition in Latin America. It was published in 1981 in Spanish, and later in English, in an anthology of articles about development and the environment Another project I worked on dealt with over-medicalization—in particular, the push to put increasing numbers of people on anti-hypertensive and cholesterol-lowering prescription drugs.

Around the same time—1978 or 1979—Lambros Comitas, my Greek American anthropologist mentor, recommended me for a fellowship to work with Rob Wasserstrom, a young professor of Anthropology at Columbia. Rob had done his field work in Mexico, and we shared a wide-ranging set of interests—social class, and health inequities in Latin America, among them. We were both bilingual and loved talking about translation and nuances in Spanish and English. We also shared a discomfort with the excesses of the chemical industry—I knew more about the pharmaceutical pushers, and Rob, because of his work in rural Mexico, knew about agricultural chemicals.

Together, we wrote an article about pesticide use in India as a factor contributing to exploding rates of malaria. When it was published in 1981 in the journal *Nature,* it created quite a stir, and it's still widely cited today. I also indexed the book that grew of Rob's dissertation on class and society in Chiapas, Mexico, and worked extensively on a volume of oral histories titled *Grassroots Development in Latin America and the Caribbean*, published in 1985.

Thinking about it now, it feels like every day was a Herculean task, but I loved everything I was doing. I was beyond ecstatic with my baby boy. I still loved my husband. I loved that we now had a house where we could invite all our musician friends to play on weekends. The women shared the cooking, the guys did the barbeque, and the kids entertained each other. On Sunday night, everyone went home, and on Monday morning, I resumed my other life—commuting into Columbia by bus (and eventually by car), finishing my coursework, hanging out with my public health and anthropology friends, and trying to ignore the signs that my marriage was in trouble.

As I began writing about this part of my life, I retrieved that oral history book from my bookcase and found this in Rob's preface and acknowledgements: "[M]y greatest debt is unquestionably owed to Georganne Chapin, who edited, corrected, proofed, scrutinized, criticized, and sharpened everything I did for nearly two full years. Obviously, there are some debts, which words like this cannot repay."

It's not only the four intervening decades that explain my surprise at seeing those words. Rather, I believe I never fully allowed myself to absorb the value or significance of what I was doing. My life at the time was utterly compartmentalized, and I was accustomed to staying within the lines of any given box, so as not to invite discord. Any pleasure or pride I would have taken for my work would have been met by my husband with profound disinterest, at best. More likely, he would have been jealous and suspicious that I must have been having an affair with Rob. What else could explain why Rob would have said those nice things? Besides, I should spend less time with my fancy university friends.

I don't think I had self-esteem issues. That wasn't the problem. No, rather it was that I was not able to be fully myself in my marriage, just as I had not been able to be fully myself in my family. My husband loved me as his musical partner and domestic partner, but he had no interest in, nor could he relate to, my academic career or any aspect of my life outside our home. In fact, he saw it all as a threat. Of course, this had been the underlying reason for me deciding to leave him in 1979. Our move into NYC, our decision to have a baby, and our next move to a house in Nyack bought the marriage and the family a few more years, but nothing was ever going to fix the fundamental differences between us. Rather than moving on, I simply compartmentalized and continued to function in separate worlds.

I'm not sure how common compartmentalization is for others, but for me, it was a way of life for decades. I think back to a conversation with my mother when I was in my 40s. In a discussion of how leaving my father affected Julia and me, she said, "You didn't miss him—but Julia did. Julia used to cry, and I even thought about going back to him, but he said no."

I remember thinking, *I didn't miss him?*

How could it be that I didn't miss my father? I was only five when my parents separated. I don't remember a lot about him, except that he was warm and funny and affectionate with me. He loved animals. And he brought me presents when he'd come home after being away on a business trip.

But even as a young child I realized my feelings were inconvenient for my mom, so I hid them. For her part, she almost never mentioned him. At one point she told me this was because she had nothing good to say about him but didn't want to malign him to his daughters. The effect was the same, perhaps. My own feelings and even any curiosity I might feel were relegated to an emotional underground, a dustbin that held fragments of me which no one wanted to explore. This was a pattern I both fell victim to and helped to perpetuate during my marriage.

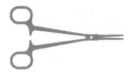

Chapter Twenty

THE MISSING PIECE

Ernesto was a wonderful baby, active, social, and engaged from the moment he was born. He crawled and then walked and talked early. Extremely gregarious, long before he could speak in complete sentences, he'd hold forth in a room full of people—babbling and gesturing in long stories that would have the entire room in stitches, despite the fact that his words were incomprehensible. He loved music, bouncing to the rhythm when his dad and I played and sang, and dragging our instruments around the house when we weren't looking.

After years of living the anthropological method—participant observer—I was all in, happily shedding the observer mantle and participating with all my heart in the experience of motherhood.

As I delighted in my child, I found that thoughts and images of my own father bubbled up frequently in my mind. Some of these were mental snapshots from my childhood (my mother had "disappeared" all photos of my father from our household). Recollections of him lifting me up to hug and kiss me when he got home from work; a memory of him bringing me an Uncle Wiggly game; and the time he took me from his car in the hospital parking lot, and we waved at my mom in an upstairs window after my sister Julia was born.

My father's name was Joseph Franklin Arthaud. He was born in Oklahoma in 1927 and raised in the Midwest (Missouri or Nebraska). He had one sister. His father and older brother were killed within one day of each other where they'd been deployed in Europe during World War II. My mother gave me few details about their marriage, in part because she was in the process of shaving a few years off her age. Once she and Hank married, she made a clean break from Joe and his family.

What she didn't hide from me is that after marrying him, she quickly found out that she and my father were not compatible. Though my mother had a sense of humor and irony, she was always a serious and modest person. My father, in contrast, was "out there"—a hilarious raconteur, grandiose and sometimes vulgar, especially when he was drinking. He was also overly and unrealistically optimistic (think gambling), highly sentimental, and moved (or fooled) by other people's hard luck stories, which more than once resulted in him lending money needed to pay the household bills. Not surprisingly, I found out later that over his lifetime he left many disappointed people in his wake.

Between 1955, when my parents separated, and 1959 when Mom, Julia, and I moved to New Mexico, I had no contact with him. Shortly after our arrival in Albuquerque, he showed up briefly to give my mother an old De Soto and a few dollars. Then, in 1961, a meeting was arranged for him to pick up Julia and me on a highway east of Albuquerque, and take us to Lubbock, Texas, to stay for a few days with him and his pregnant new wife Barbara. Inauspiciously, around the same time, my mom got a phone call from a woman who introduced herself as Barbara's mother, asking if Mom knew the whereabouts of Barbara and Joe. Apparently, Barbara had left her mother with her two children by a first marriage and disappeared with her new husband.

Shortly after our visit to Lubbock, my father relinquished custody of Julia and me. This absolved him of any obligation to pay child support (not that he had been paying, anyway) and opened the path for Hank to adopt us. It also effectively shut the door on any interactions with—or even mention of Joe Arthaud by my mother—for the rest of my childhood and beyond.

When I began thinking about finding him in the early 1980s, my urge to see my father was primarily curiosity. I wasn't curious so much about his whereabouts or his activities—but, rather, about who he was, and whether some of my own personality traits, desires, and preferences might be similar to his.

As Ernesto went from baby to toddler to little boy, every day I was struck by how much he resembled—not just in looks, but in affect and personality—relatives in both of our faraway families whom he had never met or barely knew. I saw my brother Chip (5,000 miles west in Honolulu). I saw my husband's niece Lorena (5,000 miles south in Buenos Aires).

I'd paid attention to the nature-versus-nurture debate since the 1960s, when I was in high school. Some of the families we knew in Yellow Springs were buying their daughters firetrucks and their sons dolls, believing the differences in boys and girls were primarily a result of socialization rather than biology.

The role of biology was minimized in my own household, first by papering over the fact that Hank was not my sister's and my natural father, and later—after the adoption of my Black brother Nick—by refusing to allow conversations about who in the family looked like whom. Though my mother never hurled the stereotypical child-of-divorce insult, *you're just like your father,* over the years she criticized my "excessive emotionality," my impulsive romantic attachments, and—later—my overeating. I came to realize that these were some of the same traits she hated in my father, considering them character defects.

My mother, as I have described, was a committed social activist, proudly outspoken about the causes she believed in. She also was deeply interested in the immigrant experience, writing about the Hawaii Greek community for the *Hawaiian Journal of History*, and talking about the deep losses (family, language, culture, land) that immigrants suffer when they leave their natal homes. It thus came as a shock to me when I realized she had repressed certain basic facts about herself in an effort to obscure her age and her divorce, the latter which still carried a stigma in the mid-1950s.

As a child of that divorce, I was evidence of her waywardness, so that part of my identity was similarly suppressed. Years later, when I began to understand how my mother had hidden so many events from my own past, I accused her of denying my essential identity by insisting that Hank was the only "real" father I had. She responded by telling me, "I had nothing good to say about Joe, so I said nothing at all." That wasn't really the point.

The adoption in 1967 of my brother Nicky, who was Black, was celebrated as evidence of our family's openness and diversity. Details about his parents were vague (as I learned over the years) in rather stereotypical ways. His mother was "a high school student" and his father was "in the military." His mother's relinquishment of Nick was a testament to her noble desire for him to have "a better life."

No such accolades were accorded to my father. The truths about the mother who relinquished my brother and the father who walked away from me were obscured by the needs of others who controlled the transactions and perpetuated the myths. For adopted children, this has the effect of overshadowing the needs of the child, who utterly lacks agency in the decisions being made, and has an existential (and almost always repressed) human need to know from whence she or he came.

Furthermore, the child often is expected to stay silent (as I was), and to be complicit in the myths being perpetrated either through commission or omission. My mother's gaslighting (a contemporary description of this phenomenon) of my own experiences, and the insights I have gained over time, all help to explain my later outrage at the secrecy and hypocrisy surrounding male genital cutting in American culture. The closeting, lies, and denial of the truth, and the efforts to ignore or silence the voices of the victims all occur in the service of the adults who control the narrative and perpetuate the myths.

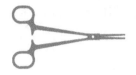

Chapter Twenty-One
GAMBLER

W hen I set out to find Joe Arthaud, I had only a bit of information. I knew he had at least one other child because Barbara had been pregnant when I last saw them. My grandmother had mentioned to me that he had called her and my uncle in Honolulu a couple of times over the years, telling them he was living in Texas.

When he called Tutu and asked her for my phone number, she refused to give it to him because, though I was away at college, I was still officially under my mom's and Hank's roof. I wish she had consulted me. When he called my Uncle Jimmy, it was to ask him to go to the airport and pick up a flight attendant my father was dating and wanted to impress with a good time in Honolulu. My grandmother eventually told me and my mother about the calls, which confirmed my mom's longstanding feelings about my father as shallow and easily wooed.

Not knowing where to start, I placed a call to a private investigator listed under "Detective Agencies" in the Manhattan Yellow Pages. John, who picked up the phone, listened to my very brief introduction: "I'm looking for my father whom I haven't seen in 25 years. He might be living in Texas or on the West Coast."

After hearing about the calls my dad had placed to my grandmother and my uncle, the PI said, "If your father isn't hiding from you, and it seems he's not, you don't need me. I'll give you some pointers on how to find him." Nice man.

Of course, in 1983 there was no such thing as the Internet. John's first suggestion was that I start with Information (411) in every area code where I thought he had lived or might be living then. To reach 411 outside my own area code entailed dialing zero and asking the operator to connect me to Information in whatever city I wanted to search.

Next, I should call the utility companies to see if now or in the past he was a customer and under what address. If the account was closed, I should ask for the forwarding address for the bills. Similarly, I should call the phone company and ask the same questions.

Finally, he said, call the police department to ask about traffic violations, arrest records, and even parking tickets.

When I asked John about confidentiality these agencies might be obliged to respect, he was dismissive: "Yeah, well, just tell them what you told me—that you're looking for your father who you haven't seen in a long time. You'll be amazed at what they'll tell you."

It didn't take much. Soon, I had a phone number for Joseph F. Arthaud in Corpus Christi, Texas.

I choked, sitting on that number for weeks before finally picking up the phone to dial. A man answered, and I hung up. I did this several times over the next six months—maybe longer. Finally, I got a recording that the number was no longer in service.

That's when I panicked. I thought, "What if he dies, and I never see him again?"

I called the phone company in Corpus Christi, and they gave me a forwarding address. I decided to write a letter. I told my father that I lived in Nyack, New York, and that I had a three-year-old son. I said I would like to hear from him and gave him my work number and my home number.

Two weeks later on a Saturday, a man called my work. My office was closed, but the administrative assistant happened to be there and answered the call. The man asked when I was expected, but he declined to give his name or leave a number. This had to have been my father, I thought.

Two more weeks passed. Finally, on a weekday, I got another call on my office phone. It was my father. I was trembling at first but calmed down as the conversation continued. He invited me to Texas to visit him and his then-wife Jackie, but I said I'd prefer he come to New York. I asked him if he had called a few weeks earlier, and he said no, that he'd only just received the letter, though it was postmarked on the day I remembered sending it.

As time passed, I came to believe that his eldest son, my half-brother Joe who was living with him at the time, must have opened it, placed that first call, and then closed the letter again and left it for my father to find.

A month or so later, I picked up my father and Jackie at LaGuardia Airport in New York City. My dad was wearing a suede sport jacket and had a big belly and a head of white hair. He looked just as I imagined he would, despite having not seen any photos of him. I could see my own face and my sister's in his.

I drove them back to Nyack, and they checked into the hotel I'd reserved. A little while later, I brought them to my home to meet Eduardo and Ernesto. The whole scene was remarkably relaxed. Ernesto loved his new grandfather. Eduardo was quite cordial to his new-found father-in-law, which I truly appreciated. He had told me half-jokingly he'd support the relationship, so long as my father didn't ask us for money. I felt at peace to finally be in the same room with him.

When we had a few moments alone, he tried to talk to me about his relationship with my mom, saying "I just want to tell you I never cheated on your mother."

Whether or not this was true, his infidelity wasn't something my mother had ever mentioned, and it seemed immaterial to me. I didn't mention that she'd told me he was an incorrigible gambler; I learned later he was quite proud of that trait!

Shortly after my father's visit, he called to tell me that his younger son Paul, ten years my junior, was moving to New York City and that we should get together. So, I now had a new half-brother to get to know. We met for the first time for lunch on the Upper West Side and then again occasionally in the city or when he paid us a visit in Nyack. Paul was strikingly handsome, with facial features and the same blond-streaked hair as my sister Julia. Until my father visited me in Nyack, Paul had no idea that Julia and I existed.

The story that unfolded of Paul's childhood, though, was sad and chaotic—alcohol, drugs, and neglect of all the three children Barbara gave birth to during her marriage to my father. He and Barbara ultimately married and divorced each other three times before finally moving on to other questionable choices.

When Paul was fifteen, my father sent him to live with Bruce, the half-brother Barbara had abandoned when she met my father around the time, my mom, Julia, and I moved to New Mexico. Not surprisingly, Bruce wasn't in any position to help even himself, let alone his younger half-brother.

Paul moved on, surviving by his good looks and his wits. He sold advertising for fashion and celebrity publications and ran with a crowd utterly unfamiliar to me. But we liked each other and, over the years, developed a strong bond.

After Paul moved to Miami and married Katherine, I attended a national health care conference at the Fontainebleau Hotel and visited them and met my newborn nephew Dylan, their first child. My father, divorced by then from Jackie, had moved from Texas to Fort Lauderdale, and his other two children with Barbara (Joe, Jr. and Allison) were also in the Miami area. Even Barbara had somehow shown up from her home in Tyler, Texas. At one point, my father said to her, "Come sit by me, Barbara, so I can pat you on the ass," and she did.

I remember thinking my mother would have been horrified. But photos from that visit show me happy, almost joyful. I clearly saw the chaos and craziness that my father had wrought and knew viscerally that my mother's escape from her marriage to him was both an act of self-preservation and a move to give her daughters a more substantive and secure future. But at the age of 33, in a strange way, I didn't care about anyone else's explanations or rationales or myths about the past. They didn't matter to me. Rather, I wanted to explore and reclaim parts of me that had been repressed during my growing-up years—my openness to all kinds of conversations, my edgy humor, my sexuality, and my almost-compulsive urge to tell the truth in the face of other people's compulsions to hide it. Despite my father's obvious transgressions and—yes—his shaky moral compass, I saw in his positive qualities some that I knew also to be among my own.

My father was truly fun. When Paul and Katherine moved to Vermont to raise their children, Ernesto and I spent many weekends and holidays with them. Paul, Katherine, and I shared a passion for Scrabble. On winter days, we'd stay in our pajamas, playing game after game, stopping only to feed my two young nephews who were being happily entertained by their cousin Ernesto. When Joe Arthaud showed up from Florida, recreational games became cut-throat competitions, complete with hilarity and frequently profane, alcohol-fueled accusations of cheating between my father and Paul. Katherine and I were into the games, but the real show was between father and son.

I was back in my familiar participant-observer role, but for once it felt appropriate. Through knowing my father, I was able to viscerally understand my mother's initial attraction to him, her growing dismay as years went by, and her conscious decision to exclude him from our lives. And I understood that their failed relationship did not need to be the only force shaping my relationship with him.

Though I had not yet become an activist, Paul, Katherine, Ernesto, and I shared our negative views on cutting boys' genitals. I knew that they had not cut either of their young boys, and Paul shared with me his outrage about having been circumcised himself when he was a baby. This was the first conversation I recall having with an adult man who talked openly and negatively about hating his circumcision. But the conversation never came up when my father was around, so I had no context for how that might have occurred.

Years passed, and I continued to see my father on occasion. He'd visit us in Nyack and spend most of his time there drinking and cooking ribs, which Ernesto loved. But the drinking, cigarettes, and barbecue were taking their toll, in the form of vascular problems and multiple heart attacks.

In late 2003, Paul and I convened at the Texas home Joe shared with his last wife Bunny. Despite being on 24-hour oxygen and knowing that the end was near, my dad was sitting on the couch when I arrived, chuckling into the phone balanced between his chin and shoulder, while holding a small spiral notebook in his left hand and a pen in his right.

"Who's he talking with?" I asked Paul.

"His bookie."

We both cracked up.

A few days later, I had to return to New York, knowing I would never see my father alive again. Paul stayed. When he called early the next week to tell me our father had passed away the night before, he added a shocker. As our dad became weaker, he asked Paul to help him in the bathroom. It was the first time Paul had seen our father's penis.

"He wasn't circumcised!" Paul told me, astonished. "Why did they do it to me?"

PART THREE:
BALANCING ACT: ADMINISTRATION, IDEALISM, ADVOCACY... AND A PERSONAL LIFE

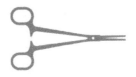

Chapter Twenty-Two

FROM STUDENT TO HEALTHCARE PROFESSIONAL

Sometimes I look back on my life and think, *How did that happen?* or *How did I do that?* It wasn't like I had a plan for my life or career. It's more that I followed my interests and instincts, and opportunities just kept coming up.

Shortly after Ernesto turned four, I decided to look for a job in health care. I'd taken my oral exams toward my PhD but couldn't imagine producing a dissertation; and I wanted to get out of the Institute for Urban and Minority Education, where I was writing and overseeing a small staff of abstractors and indexers. Though the material spoke to issues that mattered to me—racial and socioeconomic equity in education— my brief experience in Bolivia had given me an awareness that poverty and illness effectively cut off the opportunities for a good life among individuals, families, and communities. I remembered Lucila, the young mother in Mururata with her two-year-old daughter who still could not walk. I remembered Betti, who had a skin condition that didn't allow her to sleep. And while I'd hoped one day to have a career in international health, I could see that there was plenty of work to be done in communities at home, where good health and social justice were in short supply.

At the time, the Columbia School of Public Health had several divisions, including Health Administration, Population and Family Health, Epidemiology, and "my" department, Sociomedical Sciences. Truthfully, I had no clue what kind of job I might get with a master's degree in Sociomedical Sciences. I just knew what I didn't want to do—and one of those things was to become an "administrator." But I didn't have any clinical background or skills; and I wasn't headed toward a teaching career, especially without a PhD. What I envisioned was some kind of job in community health, working in a multicultural and multilingual environment, using my Spanish skills. But doing what? I wasn't sure.

One day I visited the career office at the School of Public Health and saw a posting for a temporary position at New York Medical College, just across the Hudson River from my home in Nyack. Eva Turbiner, Assistant to the President of the Medical College, was looking for a temporary replacement during her upcoming maternity leave. The job wasn't in community health, but it looked like a good start for getting to know the health care environment in the Hudson Valley where I lived. New York Med was an academic setting, but at least I would be working in something health related. Also, because I was only being hired for a few months, I would be able to openly pursue other opportunities. In the only interview (besides with Eva) I had for the job, my prospective boss, Dr. John Connolly, stressed that he'd go out of his way to introduce me to people who could be useful to me in the future. I think he was relieved to find a person who could plausibly take over from the smart and well-organized Eva.

The politics of New York Med were interesting. Founded in New York City in the mid-19th century as a school of osteopathy with a secular orientation, it had fallen on hard financial times in the 1970s. The

Catholic Archdiocese of New York had guaranteed the college's loans in exchange for being able to name some or all of the members of the Board of Directors. My boss Dr. Connolly was Irish Catholic, and there were crucifixes and pictures of the Cardinal of the Archdiocese of New York hanging in the hallways.

As Eva, who was Jewish from Pittsburgh, was showing me the ropes of her position, we talked about how the college's religious affiliation impacted its day-to-day operations (and where it did not). One of the duties listed in my job description was writing speeches for Dr. Connolly. I also would be called on to represent him at an occasional public event. Eva laughingly told me that when she'd been hired, clearly having been vetted a lot more thoroughly than I was, she was told "not to embarrass" the institution by doing anything publicly that violated Catholic doctrine. She said, "I'm not sure what that would be exactly. Having a public abortion?"

The challenges of the position intrigued me. The faculty, staff, and members of the executive administration were a diverse group that reflected the make-up of the New York metropolitan area medical community—Jews, WASPs, and Italians (the latter, obviously, mostly Catholic), and a handful of others. This was a different kind of politics from what I'd been exposed to growing up during the Civil Rights and anti-Vietnam War movement, or at the Institute for Urban and Minority Education. But ethnicity and religion influenced a lot of the college's activities, including its academic affiliations with various New York City hospitals – a world unto themselves to this day.

Eva and I kept in touch while she was on leave caring for her baby daughter. I could call and get her advice on where things were filed, what made the boss tick, and where the bodies were buried. It turned out that my original job description was rather incomplete. My day-to-day tasks ran the gamut from writing a report on the state of graduate medical education in Taiwan, to picking out the menu and table settings for a board of directors' dinner meeting, to finding a plumber to fix the toilet in the executive suite before the boss arrived the next morning. I'd never been close to the top of a large institution, and frankly, I was clueless about internal politics and the enormous influence wielded by a powerful and demanding chairman of the board of directors, not to mention the Roman Catholic Church. I came to realize that the mood of the president's office (there were four of us in the suite, in addition to the boss) could rise and fall precipitously, depending on Dr. Connolly's latest interaction with the chairman, or with the Cardinal of the Archdiocese. Although the atmosphere was frequently rather tense, it was never boring.

The most important thing I learned at New York Med was that every draft or version of what one writes must be marked with the date, and sometimes even the time of day. Eva had left folders of reports, and I'd often find three different versions marked "final," no doubt reflecting Dr. Connolly's most recent round of edits. I'm pretty sure if you ask the people who've worked for me over the last 35 years about my pet peeves, most of them will tell you, "She hates grammatical errors and she wants a date, title, and author on everything."

The job was relatively close to home, I had good day care for Ernesto, and—after so many years of juggling school, work, music, and my marriage—the strains in my personal life eased a bit. There was no Rob Wasserstrom for my husband to be jealous of, the hours were regular, and I wasn't expected to and didn't want to socialize after hours with my co-workers. The Hudson Valley, where we'd moved in 1980, was starting to feel more like home.

After a few months, it became clear that Eva wasn't planning to come back. She confided to me that she was interviewing for other positions and secured one shortly before her return date. I had never planned to stay beyond the nine-month period we originally agreed upon, and—true to his word—Dr. Connolly had been introducing me to people who might be in positions to offer me a job. When he offered me the Assistant to the President position on a permanent basis, I thanked him but told him what I'd known before – that I wanted to work in community health.

Chapter Twenty-Three

SEEKING JUSTICE

In 1985, I took a job as an ambulatory care planner at the Hudson Valley Health Systems Agency (HSA), which opened a path to the next three decades of my work life. My role was to understand and document health care services in the region offered by public health departments, community health centers, and other outpatient settings.

The issue that most fired me up was maternity care. New York's liberal maternal and infant health program guaranteed payment to doctors for prenatal, delivery, and post-partum care—even for women who had no insurance and were unable to pay for these services. Despite this, during the time I was at the HSA, the dearth of doctors willing to give maternal care and deliver the babies of poor and minority women reached scandalous proportions. Getting a timely appointment was next to impossible, and then a mom would be labeled "non-compliant" because of "late entry into prenatal care."

Hospitals were also complicit. Here's an example: using the excuse that such women were high risk, one (not-for-profit) inpatient facility located in the most blighted neighborhood of Newburgh, New York, routinely either turned away poor women who arrived in labor or transported them by ambulance 50 miles to the region's only public hospital.

I didn't have the diplomatic skills needed to give a calm, neutral-sounding analysis about this travesty. After one phone call with the health reporter for a local newspaper, he accurately quoted me as saying that the county health commissioner (also a member of the local physician community) wasn't doing his job. He wasn't. To her credit, the head of the planning agency (my boss) only mildly admonished me after receiving an irate call from that health commissioner.

The worst thing about the job was that the planning agency was extremely underfunded. This impacted both the quality of my work life and any aspirations I had of actually making a difference. The HSA headquarters occupied the first floor of a mouse-infested office building in the middle of the woods in the middle of nowhere—a ludicrous location equally inconvenient to any other spot in the seven-county region we covered. Because travel funds were limited, in my 11 months on the job I spent most of my time on the phone with health care administrators, county officials, and reporters discussing contentious issues such as hospitals pushing to acquire high-tech equipment and build fancy emergency departments, while so many people throughout the region lacked access to the most basic medical care.

Limiting travel was one thing. But having the executive director come into my office when I was on the phone with a newspaper reporter or a clinic director to pantomime me ending the call—because the agency had only two phone lines for a staff of 12—was quite another. *If this organization can't even afford telephone lines, how can we be expected to do our jobs?* My frustration mounted daily.

Not so many years later, when I was running my own nonprofit organization, my experience at the HSA, as well as respect for professional staff members' autonomy, led to my insistence that they be given the resources they needed to perform well. My belief was, and is, there's no honor in mediocrity. My mantra became *if we cannot make a meaningful difference with the funds and resources we have available, then we should just close up and go home.*

The stimulating part of the health planning job, though, was getting to know the organizations and the people who were doing the type of work I'd begun envisioning during my field study in the mountains of Bolivia. Even with the HSA's restricted travel policy, I eked out a few site visits to the region's community health centers—places I'm embarrassed to admit I'd never known about.

In the mid-1980s, the community health centers in the Hudson Valley were led by truly interesting and unusual people—all kick-ass women who had come to the work with public health or nursing backgrounds and as community activists in the civil rights movement and the War on Poverty. Unlike my boss at the HSA, who had fallen victim to a scarcity mindset of two phone lines for a dozen staff members, these women embodied the health care and social justice ideals I'd become nearly obsessed with. They viewed challenges as *opportunities* to overcome.

One day as I sat at my desk in the mouse-infested HSA, I took a call from Marge Griesmer. Marge was the founder and executive director of a health center serving low-income residents of Ossining, New York, a small city on the banks of the Hudson River. I'd visited Marge at Ossining Open Door a few weeks before, and, as we chatted, she had asked me what kind of work I wanted to do in the future. I said, "I want to make basic medical care a right—not a privilege—for people who are poor, who are discriminated against, or who don't speak English."

In a pattern I have come to recognize as a recurring theme in my life, Marge apparently set her sights on me as someone to bring into the fold.

She explained the purpose of her call: "We're hiring an executive director for the Westchester Health Network, the coalition of the four community health centers in the county. I want you to apply."

"Marge," I answered, "Thank you, but I can't leave the HSA. I haven't even been here a year."

"So what?" she replied. "You told me you were bored and felt you weren't doing anything meaningful. You'd be perfect for this job. You can work with all of us and help the health centers to grow. You need to do this."

I thanked her again, said I'd apply, and agreed to send her a resumé—and did nothing further about it. I was paralyzed by the routine of being in the middle of nowhere day after day, cranking out analyses and recommendations that also were likely to go nowhere.

Three weeks later, Marge called again. "Georganne, the interviews for that job are tonight. I just found out you never applied, so I called David Ford and told him about you. David is the chairman of the Mount Vernon Neighborhood Health Center and the chairman of the coalition. He's leading the interviews. You're scheduled for the last slot of the evening, so you have plenty of time to get there. Just take your resumé with you."

Chapter Twenty-Four
A PATH APPEARS

I went home, had dinner with Eduardo and Ernesto, and headed for Mount Vernon. In addition to Mr. Ford, the board chairmen and some of the community board members from the four health centers in the coalition were sitting in chairs lining the room on three sides.

Some had been prepped with pro-forma questions about whether I was familiar with certain federal reporting requirements (I was not). Nobody asked whether I had any business, finance, or managerial experience (I did not). But both Mr. Ford and Ossining Open Door's board chairman, a filmmaker and philanthropist named Martin Low, wanted to know about my philosophy and commitment to community health and equity. Mr. Ford also zeroed in on my resumé, commenting how impressed he was with my Barnard College degree and my graduate studies at Columbia. I thanked them all as I left the room and they remained to discuss the candidates they'd interviewed that evening. I was intrigued, but still of the mindset that I wasn't ready to change jobs.

The next morning at the HSA my phone rang shortly before 9 a.m. "Georganne, this is David Ford. I want to offer you the job as executive director of the Westchester Health Network. The search committee members all agreed. You are our first choice."

Wow, that was easy, I remember thinking. *Now, the hard part is deciding if I want to do it.* We briefly discussed a possible start date and salary, and I asked Mr. Ford for a couple of days to get back to him.

Not 15 minutes later the phone rang again. It was Marge. "Martin Low [her board chairman] told me they are going to hire you. When can you start?"

"I have to give notice," I replied, forgetting that a few minutes earlier I wasn't sure whether I wanted the job or not. "So probably in around a month." I called Mr. Ford that afternoon and told him I accepted. The position paid roughly the same as my HSA salary, $27,000 annually.

Just a few days later, I encountered Martin who, unbeknownst to me, also held a seat on the regional volunteer health planning council. He greeted me with great enthusiasm: "I'm just delighted that you'll be running the Network," he said. "But if you had turned down that job, I was going to ask you if you'd like to be the head of a new nonprofit Medicaid HMO that the health centers are starting." Despite the fact that many of the players were the same, no one had mentioned this other project during the brief conversations about the activities of the coalition.

"That sounds interesting," I answered. "Tell me more about it."

Martin was very smart and well-read. Like me, he believed that intelligent management of needed medical services, combined with a commitment to justice and health equity, could help solve racial, social, and economic disparities in access to health care. In our conversation, he described the underlying philosophy of the new managed care program, the federal and state funding sources, and tasks for getting the new insurance company up and running. He finished by saying the committee doing the hiring still hadn't found a proper candidate.

"I might be able to help you," I responded, thinking of Eva, whose place I'd taken two years earlier at New York Medical College. "I have a friend working at Einstein [Albert Einstein School of Medicine], and she might be interested. How much does the position pay?"

"Between fifty and fifty-five thousand," he replied.

Now, this was double the salary I'd just accepted for another executive position working for the same group of health centers and an overlapping board of directors. And Martin, chairman of the board of the new HMO, thought I was qualified for that job, too.

But I'd accepted the job offered to me by David Ford. And, in all honesty, I wasn't altogether confident in my ability or experience to start a brand-new company.

"If you can get me the job description," I told Martin, "I'll reach out to her."

We parted cheerfully, with Martin assuring me that as head of the coalition I'd be at the table during the planning meetings for the new HMO.

As I wrapped things up at the HSA, I began to feel excited about working in a real-life community health environment. My office would be located in the Mount Vernon Neighborhood Health Center, on the mostly Black, mostly low income South side of that city, bordering the New York City borough of the Bronx. I'd be flanked by the offices of Mr. Ford and Ms. Carole Morris, the legendary nurse and activist who had been instrumental in organizing the community, securing the funding for the Mount Vernon facility, and shepherding its construction. Carole—like Marge Griesmer—was known as someone who never took "no" for an answer.

A few years later, when I was running the health plan, the then-chairman of my board of directors told me that an administrator from the federal agency that regulated the Community Health Centers had referred to Marge, Carole, and the directors of the other two health centers in the coalition as "the four witches of Westchester."

I heard misogyny, but I also heard respect for the nearly magical powers of these women to get things done. They had to be tough in order to find funding, get their facilities built, hire, train and manage staff, and meet all the state and federal rules and regulations—all while managing their own homes and family lives. They also maintained a unified front for the purpose of lobbying, though they fought mercilessly among themselves as they competed for resources and acclaim.

The political, interpersonal, and racial dynamics of the health center world both intrigued me and provided dramatic accents to the day-to-day work. So, this was what people meant by "politics" with a small "p." My colleagues, as both board members and my bosses, were as admirable as they were difficult.

My formal job tasks for the Westchester Health Network, though, were minimal. The coalition served as the grantee for federal community health center funds, and my role was to submit the four centers' annual plans, attest to their compliance with all applicable regulations, and then distribute the checks once the grant came in. I had two full-time staff members—a bookkeeper and a secretary. I reported to a board of directors made up of representatives from each of the four Community Health Centers. The position of Board Chairman rotated every couple of years among the four health center chairmen.

As mentioned above, when I began, David Ford was chairman of both the coalition and the Mount Vernon center. Mr. Ford had been born in Guyana and came to the United States as a teenager during World War II and enlisted in the Army. When I met him and for years thereafter, he was the most influential Black political leader in Westchester County and also held an appointment as Mount Vernon's Water Commissioner, spanning the tenure of several Mayors. The walls of his Health Canter office were covered with awards, the shelves were full of trophies, and he greatly enjoyed greeting visitors there. David wore a gun strapped to his ankle, and when we would go out for an occasional lunch in a local restaurant, he'd insist on sitting at a back table, facing the front door.

Sometimes on school holidays, I'd take my son to the Mount Vernon office, and he and Mr. Ford would sit and chat. Just six years old at the time but with the social instincts of a politician himself, Ernesto was quite impressed with David's trophies, his stories, and his gregarious persona. Several years later, after I'd moved my organization to another location, I encountered David at a social event. Ernesto, by then ten or eleven years old, was with me, and David greeted him heartily. Leaning close, he said something to David which I couldn't hear, to which David burst out laughing. "Absolutely!" he exclaimed.

On the way home, I asked Ernesto, "What did you ask Mr. Ford?"

"I asked him if he's still packing."

Chapter Twenty-Five

THE ACCIDENTAL INSURANCE CEO

I had learned a lot about how not to manage an organization from my experience at the HSA. But I learned more about being a leader from David Ford than from anyone I ever worked for. David engendered great respect in everyone who met him. He was smart, observant, and genial. What I most appreciated, though, was his no-nonsense directness. If he was unhappy with something I had done, he'd tell me, and he'd tell me why.

My mistakes in those days were almost always related to my impatience, lack of diplomacy, and my too-frequent failure to think through the consequences of a quick retort. I also learned from David that everything in our world was potentially political and demanded forethought. He never turned me away if I wanted to run a question or problem by him—for example, before making or taking a delicate phone call.

When I screwed something up, David would usually ask to see me in person, and would tell me—in a few pointed words—what was bothering him. He was almost always on target. He'd then listen to my explanation or apology, and we would talk about how I might have handled the situation differently. Then we would move on. We remained friendly for many years.

I loved my job. I loved how crazy and messy it was. I loved learning about the different histories and inner workings of the health centers. I found the racial politics more interesting and challenging than intimidating. Two of the health center directors were white, two were Black, and their communities were experiencing rapidly increasing numbers of immigrants from the Caribbean and Central and South America. The size and demographics of the patient population went into the health centers' federal and state funding formulas, and at meetings the directors' mutual accusations of misrepresenting those statistics flew around the room.

One meeting among coalition members, held during a national health center conference in Washington, D.C., stands out in my memory. The four health center directors, along with Chairman Ford and me, met in a hotel suite to discuss the most recent funding application to the federal Health Resources Services Administration (HRSA). The director who had asked for the meeting accused another of lying about the number of patients and patient visits at her sites.

The accused director began to cry—a tactic I had seen her use before, but only when a man was present. She looked beseechingly at David, as if to say, "Defend me!" He was unmoved. All of us just sat there, until she realized that she would get no sympathy from anyone present. Suddenly, she changed her mood from pleading and pathetic to angry and insulting, telling her accuser, "We'll leave you in the dust." The meeting quickly broke up.

Somehow, I managed to maintain a decent relationship with each of the four directors, even as they fought and jockeyed for influence and money for their centers. Most far reaching was my realization that the actual technical skills required for working in community health—or, for that matter, any job at the nexus of government, the people, and the business of medicine—were minimal when compared to one's ability to navigate the interpersonal, social, and organizational politics.

When I began at Westchester Health Network, Medicaid managed care delivered by community health centers was a growing model around the country designed to provide better care for poor people. New York was an early adopter of the model. Financing worked like this: instead of doctors and hospitals billing the state for every visit, every procedure, every service, the state would pay a monthly lump sum to the insurer. The insurer would then negotiate prices with the "providers" and make sure that they were billing properly, and (theoretically) only for necessary services. "Privatizing" Medicaid supposedly would result in better care and lower overall costs.

Eva—whom I'd successfully recruited as the first executive director of the HMO—began work just a few months after I started at the coalition. She opened a new office and, because we answered to the same board members and dealt with the same group of community health center directors, we worked together closely from the beginning. I had taken it upon myself to add a number of tasks, aside from packaging their annual submission to the feds and writing a few checks, to my work for the health center directors. I particularly liked writing grant proposals, because I got to meet other staff members from the centers and learn more about the work they were doing.

After a year or so, Eva and I decided it made sense to combine our offices and jointly leased space near the center of the county. Not too long after we pooled our respective organizations' funds for our offices, the lease for our copying machine, and the salary of a receptionist, Eva announced she was pregnant with her second child and planned to resign from the health plan. At the December 1988 meeting of the board of directors, as a result of conversations that, it became obvious, had taken place behind the scenes, Mr. Ford offered me the position as executive director of the organization that would under my leadership become Hudson Health Plan.

Thus, I would now have the position and salary that Martin Low (still on the board) had casually offered me more than two years earlier. My official start date was just a couple of weeks later, January 1, 1989. I would also continue to head up the Westchester Health Network, though pretty much everyone knew its days were numbered because the constituent health centers had grown apart.

When I assumed my new role, the managed care plan operated in just one county and had just 800 members, six employees, and annual revenue of around $250,000. Twenty-five years later, when the CEO of a large commercial insurance company approached me with a takeover proposal, Hudson Health Plan had nearly 150,000 members in six counties, nearly 350 employees, and annual revenue of nearly $800 million.

The road to this success was facilitated by national and state health care policy changes, and was paved with hard work by many people, an enormous amount of satisfaction, and a few near-disasters—the first which occurred four weeks into my new job.

Before resigning from the health plan, Eva had hired a new finance director. The previous person in that position had left a couple of months earlier, which—together with Eva's resignation—should have given me a heads-up. But, as I've already said, my business training was nil, and any business acumen had yet to be born.

Just after the first January pay-day, H, as I'll call him here, came to my office, closed the door behind him, sat down, and announced: "We are broke. We have two payrolls in the bank."

"What do you mean," I responded. "I thought the bank balance was over $300,000."

"It is," he answered. "But ninety-five percent of that money is obligated to the health centers through our surplus-sharing contracts."

Surplus-sharing is a concept that—in the early days of HMOs—was sacrosanct. The underlying premise was that if doctors could save the insurer money by keeping patients healthy, those doctors would be rewarded with a share of the surplus. For the new health plan I was running, the upshot was that after just one year of operation, the health centers wanted 95 percent of the surplus, as their contracts specified. And I was confronted with the real possibility that the new organization would fizzle and die.

Re-enter Martin Low—who had just rotated into the chairmanship of the health plan. I called Martin and told him I needed to see him urgently. He, H, and I met away from my small office, so we could talk without fear of being overheard by staff members who would—understandably—find the conversation disconcerting. After we told Martin about the vanishing-surplus situation, he sat back in his chair and said, "The state [New York State Department of Health, or DOH] is responsible for this. They approved the contracts."

Martin knew this because he'd been on the board since the beginning. He was aware of the health centers' insistence on capturing all of the surplus and Eva's relative lack of negotiating power with her board of directors. "So," he continued, "let's go talk with the people at DOH."

I made the call and set up a meeting.

The meeting was hosted by two guys in the newly created Medicaid managed care division of the New York State Department of Health. I won't name them, but I will say that not too much later, one was buying a food truck and selling hotdogs. The other, whom I'll call Mr. T, remained active in the health insurance industry for many years.

Martin and I explained our dilemma, citing the fact that nearly all of the health plan's funds were obligated under the ninety-five percent surplus-sharing arrangement in our contracts with the health centers. The only possible "out" was a clause in the contract saying the DOH had the discretion to disallow any distribution should it threaten the financial stability of the health plan. The health centers knew about this but had assumed the approval was a mere formality.

"Who on earth approved those contracts?" Mr. T asked incredulously.

I handed him a copy of the contract approval letter from DOH, emblazoned with his signature at the bottom of the page. He and the hot dog truck guy looked at each other.

"All right." Mr. T said without missing a beat. "I'll tell you what to do. You write me a letter saying you plan to distribute the funds as per the contracts. I'll write back and tell you we can't approve the distribution, and I'll add that the contracts need to be renegotiated with a more equitable surplus-sharing arrangement between the health centers and the health plan."

It worked.

Chapter Twenty-Six

THE DEMISE OF MY MARRIAGE

Just a few weeks after I assumed leadership of Hudson Health Plan, Eduardo, Ernesto, and I moved into a brick ranch home in Upper Nyack, New York. Ernesto was eight years old.

Between the first Nyack house and this one, we'd briefly relocated to the northwestern part of Rockland County. I'd found, though, that the extra fifteen miles each way on the crowded Tappan Zee Bridge, added as much as ninety minutes to my round-trip commute. We were all happy to be back in "the Nyacks," as locals referred to the string of villages along the river.

But my marriage was in serious trouble. Eduardo's drinking had gotten worse, and his growing and generalized hostility toward me had also begun to show up in his interactions with our son. What had for years been a loving father-son relationship, punctuated by an occasional spat, noticeably deteriorated as Ernesto became more independent.

When we married, I harbored hopes that Eduardo would embrace the educational and other opportunities that had eluded him in Argentina. He was so smart, and so talented musically. He was hard-working, handsome, charming, and modest—all qualities that, to me, positioned him for success and a happy life. But, as I began to see, this wasn't a simple matter of having a supportive partner and the resources to enroll in a community college. Writing this, I recognize how clueless I had been at age twenty-three.

I knew my husband was undereducated, and that he had serious dyslexia that had caused him to be branded "lazy" and slow to learn in school. I also knew he'd left his home in Buenos Aires in 1972 under a cloud. But, probably because of my own romanticism, rather than anything he told me to the contrary, I believed it was economic hardship and political turmoil that had exiled him. Those factors certainly figured in. However, over the years we were together, I began to see and feel his hidden demons from an upbringing I had known nothing about when we married.

This knowledge trickled in slowly, because (like my own parents and siblings in Hawaii), my Argentine in-laws lived 5,000 miles away. With limited phone service in the 1970s and 1980s, limited money to travel, and Facetime and Zoom still decades away, our opportunities to interact came, at most, every three or four years, for a few weeks at a time. The exception was an occasional visit from my mother-in-law, Doña Mari, a kind woman who had repressed her own needs and personality throughout her entire life.

Shortly after Eduardo and I met in New York, his father died in an accident in Argentina. I knew that much. But I did not know the back story, which unspooled over years.

Eduardo had grown up in a household plagued by an angry, verbally abusive father and a passive mother. Tomás, Eduardo's father, was a professed atheist who treated his wife with contempt because of her Roman Catholic beliefs and the time she spent praying and in church. Eduardo, like his father, was an adamant atheist with moral positions as inflexible as those of a rigid Catholicism.

Because Eduardo wasn't a womanizer, and didn't mind cooking or doing dishes, for years it never occurred to me to see his behavior and attitudes as misogynistic. But misogyny ran deep in the Echeverria family, epitomized by a father who ranted and raved and cursed and a mother who lowered her head and bit her lip, rather than speak up to defend herself or her children.

Eduardo's sister Iris, the youngest of the three siblings, had become the target of their father's misogynistic rants, which became more and more obsessive, and even vulgar, as she entered adolescence. Eduardo, for his part, told me frequently that his father was a "saint," and that his sister was the one to blame for the chronic discord in the household. I found this all quite confusing.

Eduardo also told me that not too long before he left Argentina, he had become violently angry at his sister and threatened her with bodily harm. Shortly after that, when a childhood friend announced that he was leaving to look for work in New York, Eduardo's mother encouraged him to go along, saying, "There's nothing but trouble for you here."

The way he framed that story was to blame his sister for his mother "kicking him out of the house." The death of their father two years later occurred after his sister ran away from home to live with a boyfriend, and her father left the house half-crazed to track her down. While riding his bike along a major highway, he was hit by a truck and died two days later. In 1977, Eduardo and I went together to Argentina to visit his family, and I witnessed a terrible scene in the kitchen—with Eduardo screaming at Iris, accusing her of their father's death, and telling her she should die. His mother saw it all and never said a word. I am ashamed to say that neither did I, not then or ever.

It's hard for me to explain now, nearly fifty years later, what I was thinking during the early years of our marriage. I had plenty of unresolved emotional issues myself. But, whether from naiveté, an inflated sense of my ability to handle troubled relationships, or simple inertia, I continued to insist we could get beyond our "cultural differences" and the traumas of our respective upbringings and create a healthy family life.

I was wrong.

Unresolved family conflicts, Eduardo's profound feelings of oppression, and his increasing consumption of alcohol over the course of our marriage hardened into a rage that was never far from the surface. More than once, I suggested marriage counseling or family therapy. Having begun to see a therapist myself, I believed that a knowledgeable and compassionate practitioner could help Eduardo to understand the dynamics of his childhood and get beyond them. But as time went on, I became increasingly sure that our marriage was doomed. My response was to keep on compartmentalizing, something I know now did not serve either our son or me well.

Eduardo's main complaint about Ernesto, born in New York City and raised in a middle-class suburban community, was that he was "too American." It seemed to me that my son's father was emotionally and psychologically stuck in working-class Argentina of the 1950s and 1960s.

In a dynamic I've come to understand better over the years, like many immigrant parents, Eduardo was unable to appreciate the diversity and opportunities the United States offered to his child, without feeling that his own customs and identity were threatened. For whatever reason, perhaps because in Hawaii the Greeks were so few in number that they were forced to interact with non-Greeks, this was not a pattern I had observed in my mother's upwardly mobile extended family.

Thus, for years a loving father, Eduardo began to treat his son with increasing harshness as he became older and more independent. Rather than seeing Ernesto's growing circle of friends and independent interests as positive, and a normal part of his development, Eduardo viewed these changes as representing a rejection of his father and his Argentinian heritage.

Nothing could have been further from reality. Ernesto adored and idolized his father. He wanted to emulate Eduardo's language and demeanor, and from toddlerhood spoke Spanish as well as English. He enthusiastically embraced Argentine culture and music and spent several summers with his extended family in Buenos Aires. A marvel of sociability, Ernesto has always been able to connect and find common ground with people of all ages and cultures, and all walks of life. He loved telling people he was Argentine and showing off his language skills and ecumenical knowledge of Latin American music.

To Eduardo, though, his son's gregariousness and the fact that he also loved Michael Jackson, Michael Jordan, the Beastie Boys, and *The Simpsons* meant he was betraying his Argentine roots.

My own career development—as my parents had predicted fifteen years before—also had become an increasing source of tension and conflict in my marriage. What I characterized earlier as "compartmentalizing" could now be described as conducting a separate life on parallel tracks. One track was our home and musical life. The other was my work as a health care executive with a demanding and absorbing job. I also maintained relationships with friends from my college and grad school days, two of whom (Barbara and Bob) Ernesto still thinks of as his aunt and uncle. And, because my parents and siblings were so far away, I maintained close ties with Hank's family in western New York, spending many Thanksgivings with my Chapin grandparents, aunts, and uncles.

My friends and family members all embraced Eduardo. He was smart and could be wickedly funny. My grandparents even commented that, with his fair hair and complexion, Eduardo blended right in with their clan. Little could they have imagined that when we returned home after a pleasant weekend, he would launch into a diatribe about how the Chapins looked down on him. This was untrue. But as was happening with our son, if there was something Eduardo didn't understand or appreciate, he dismissed it as pretentious or as designed to devalue or undermine him.

Shortly after we moved to Upper Nyack in early 1989, I confided in a close friend the truth about my crumbling marriage. Every day as the tension grew, I felt I was simply marking time and that things were heading toward a breaking point. Something happened one spring day in 1991 that made me realize I needed to act.

Our house was full of musical instruments—guitars, flutes, wooden drums, fiddles, and more. Most of them we played, but some—in various states of utility or disrepair—had been given to us by friends, or we'd picked them up ourselves at yard sales or in local antique shops. For months, an old violin had been propped up on the mantel above the fireplace, and I'd noticed that the front plate had begun to separate from the rib (the side of the body). Nobody ever played that fiddle. Had I given it any thought, I would have assumed Eduardo knew it needed fixing and that he'd get around to doing that at some point.

One day, as he passed through the living room, he noticed the crack, apparently for the first time. He took the violin down, held it up close to my face, and demanded, "Who broke this?"

"Nobody broke it," I said. "It just separated—probably from the dry heat in the house."

"No, you dropped it, and you don't want to admit it."

"I didn't drop it!" I answered, still not realizing how agitated he had become.

And then I made the mistake of involving my son, nearly eleven by then. "Ernesto," I called out. "Did you see the crack in the violin on the mantel?"

He wandered into the living room. "Yeah," he shrugged. "It's been like that forever. I don't know what happened to it."

Eduardo's face went bright red as he turned to me. "Why should I believe him?" He spit out the words. "He's a liar just like you."

My husband had called me a liar before—for example, when I'd told him I'd been stuck in traffic driving home. And during the early years of our marriage, when he would accuse me of having affairs with my work colleagues, I'd beg him to trust me. But at some point, I had told him simply to stop with the accusations—and that if he really felt I was unfaithful or untruthful, then he shouldn't be married to me. And it had stopped, for the most part.

But now, here we were again, and the target was not just me, but my son. And my reaction was visceral. To hear Ernesto's father attack him in this way sickened me. For the first time in sixteen years, I lost control of myself, and hurled a plate after him as he headed for the door. He came back, shoved me into a wall, told me he'd wring my throat, and then—thankfully—turned and left the house. Ernesto witnessed the entire episode.

During the escalating arguments leading up to that one, Eduardo had said many times that, so far as he was concerned, the marriage was over. "I hate you and you hate me. We need to separate." But the words were often spoken when he was drunk, and the next day it was as though nothing had happened. I'd propose marriage counseling. He'd refuse. I'd then broach the subject of finding a lawyer and working out finances and child custody and visitation. He'd look at me like I was crazy.

Now I saw it was not safe for us to stay together, and I knew I had to be the one to make a move.

A few days after the violin incident, I took the afternoon off from work and went home, packed a suitcase with some clothes, my flutes, an antique piccolo I'd bought in Argentina, and some photo albums. These were all things I feared he might destroy when he discovered we were gone. I also packed a bag for Ernesto. I drove to Upper Nyack Elementary as the school day was ending and told the principal that Ernesto would be out for a few days and why. We went to a hotel with a swimming pool around ten miles away.

I asked my friend Barbara to call Eduardo and tell him that I wouldn't be coming back to the house with Ernesto so long as he was there. She also conveyed to him that I wanted to work out how he and Ernesto could see each other elsewhere until we had some kind of formal agreement. I was not suffering for myself. I'd known for years my marriage was doomed but just didn't have the courage to leave. But I was suffering—and continued to suffer greatly for a long time—for my son. Tragically, over the next months and years, Eduardo transferred his rage about the end of our marriage to Ernesto, tainting his adolescence and beyond.

Chapter Twenty-Seven
SINGLE WORKING MOM

I'd known for years, even before the birth of my son, that my marriage was unlikely to last and that I was the one who was going to have to end it. Moving back to Nyack bought us a brief reprieve, but over the next couple of years, the bonds that had held Eduardo and me together were deteriorating, falling away, and I had been mourning the losses, piece by piece.

We also had almost entirely stopped performing publicly and seldom played music together at home. The pressure I felt to make music with him was akin to the pressure I felt to have sex with him, and neither was working. To quote Gordon Lightfoot's song *If You Could Read my Mind*: "...the feeling's gone and I just can't get it back."

The argument over the broken violin was the last straw. I mostly felt relief. Details of the days, weeks, and even months immediately following my flight from the house with Ernesto remain blurred in my mind, with a few exceptions. Between recriminations and insults (*just because I called you a whore a few times doesn't give you the right to leave me* still sticks in my mind), eventually we managed to negotiate that I would move back into the house, at least for the time being. Eduardo rented an apartment in downtown Nyack, which meant that Ernesto could ride his bike to visit his father.

The empty space in the driveway where he used to park his silver Toyota pickup felt like a gift when I arrived home at the end of the workday. Little things like not hearing him rant about the neighbor who didn't pick up after her dogs when she walked along our property (somehow implying it was my responsibility to confront her) were a huge relief. No longer did I have to wonder when he'd fly off the handle about something I viewed, at worst, as a minor inconvenience. I didn't have to listen to his bitter dinner table complaints about his job and his coworkers. Nor did I have to watch him become more agitated by the minute as he poured himself glass after glass of red wine.

But once he was no longer able to take his anger and frustration out on me, Eduardo directed it at Ernesto as a way to continue making me miserable. He would call me in the evenings and berate me about how I had "ruined" our son. I would argue: "How can you say that? What do you mean he's ruined?" I was constantly kept off balance by his phone calls that I did not have the presence of mind (or the courage) to ignore. Too often, Ernesto would hover in the kitchen, listening to the drama. It was horrible.

The first Christmas after we separated, my friend Rachel invited Ernesto and me to spend the day with her family. Ernesto, though, had made plans with his dad. So, after Eduardo picked him up, I went on my own to Rachel's house, half an hour away in New Jersey.

Around one o'clock in the afternoon, something made me call home to check messages. Instead of the answering machine, though, Ernesto picked up the phone. Shocked, I asked him why he was not at his dad's. In tears, he told me Eduardo had accused him of only wanting to visit that day to get his Christmas presents.

Ernesto related his father's exact words: "Now that you've got your presents, I'm taking you back to the house your mother stole from me."

And with that, my estranged husband had dropped off our 11-year-old son to spend the rest of Christmas day alone. I thanked the stars for my maternal intuition nudging me to make that phone call. I made a beeline to Nyack to retrieve a devastated Ernesto. We returned to New Jersey for dinner, but that was a sad day.

I cannot access from my memory many of the details of the first couple of years after my separation from Eduardo. What I am able to remember, though, is colored by a mix of feelings—relief, anxiety, and pain for my son. My job meant I often did not arrive home until after six. Though Ernesto and I had dinner together every night (sometimes I cooked, and sometimes we went out), it disturbed me that no loving parent was present when Ernesto arrived home from school and fixed himself a snack. It bothered me more when I discovered a pack of cigarettes in the bathroom cabinet.

Always a student who had marched to the rhythm of his own drum, Ernesto was having trouble adjusting to the local middle school, and I felt he could use more attention from his teachers. Fortunately, with my parents' financial help, I was able to enroll him in a nearby private day school with small classes and a more flexible schedule (having time to eat a snack between classes was a big plus for a kid with labile blood sugar). While I felt this was the right decision for Ernesto, it only served to further alienate his father who, despite having struggled himself in school at that age, labeled me (and, by association, his son) as pretentious because of the move to a private school.

At home, my relationship with Ernesto was fairly harmonious. Our conflicts mostly revolved around homework and improved for a time with the change of venue. Also, he insisted he had "quit" smoking at the age of 12, and I chose to believe him. But he spent a lot of hours each day watching MTV and not doing his homework. In exasperation, I cut off cable service, saying, "I can't make you do your schoolwork, but I can take away *that* distraction."

He didn't improve much as a student, but boredom pushed him out-doors, and he began riding his bicycle everywhere, even finding a job at a fancy bike shop in a town just south of us. He'd ride the six miles to work after school a couple of days a week; usually, I'd pick him up and drive him both ways on weekends. This was the beginning of a love affair with cycling and the acquisition of bicycle repair and retail sales skills that gave him a new group of peers, as well as income, for most of the next two decades.

But Eduardo continued to haunt our household, with my son having to navigate the same drinking, unpredictable moods and grievances that had plagued the last years of my marriage and our family life. I also was aware that Eduardo said terrible things to my son about me and my family. While Ernesto knew on one level that this came from a place of bitterness and irrationality, I know it caused him a lot of confusion and hurt, too.

Eduardo also became increasingly alienated from his own family in Argentina, seemingly bitter that they maintained a relationship with me —something I felt grateful for. I loved my sister-in-law, her husband, and my nephews, in particular, and thought it benefited Ernesto to be able to visit there with my cooperation, but Eduardo seemed intent on poisoning the well.

So, while my life went on without the day-to-day household conflict with my husband, I never felt at peace. I worried when the phone rang and when Ernesto made plans with Eduardo. I worried that he wouldn't follow through and my son would be left hanging and I worried about the long-term effects of all this on my son.

We had good times, too, though. My half-brother Paul and his wife were living in Vermont, and we'd visit them there, hang out, and play Scrabble. We made regular trips to Hawaii to see family, and Ernesto became intrigued with Hawaiian culture, especially the native tattooing traditions. And he participated in my work life, getting to know the health plan staff, and learning the lingo, and even some of the ins and outs, of our industry. Even at 12 years old, Ernesto took a proprietary pride in the success of Hudson Health Plan.

One day when we arrived home after dinner, he punched the flashing button on the kitchen answering machine and we listened to a lengthy message from a candidate running for a seat in the state legislature. Near the end, the candidate promised to "bring down the HMOs that are ruining our health care system." Ernesto stepped back from the phone and declared, "Take down the HMOs? Thanks to an HMO," he gestured dramatically toward our kitchen window and backyard, "I have all this!"

By early 1993, it was clear that we needed to move the health plan out of the small suite Eva and I had rented together four years earlier and find something more suitable for our growing company. Under the leadership of New York Governor Mario Cuomo, New York established an insurance program called Child Health Plus. Unlike Medicaid, which required that recipients be citizens or legal permanent residents of the United States, Child Health Plus covered children regardless of their immigration status. And depending on the family's income, it was either extremely inexpensive or even free.

Hudson Health Plan's service area had seen an enormous increase in immigrants from various Latin American countries, and Child Health Plus

(CHP) now meant we had something unique and very valuable to offer. Our marketing staff, including the leaders of that department, were mostly bilingual (Spanish/English). We immediately launched a CHP enrollment campaign, and our numbers and revenue (paid by the state) shot up.

With the approval of my board of directors, I leased office space in Tarrytown, in a building overlooking the Hudson River. For the first time in my career, I was working with architects and interior designers to plan and configure an office for an organization that promised to outpace our most ambitious early projections. The new office was just 15 minutes from my home in Nyack, unless the Tappan Zee bridge was backed up, in which case the trip still took less than a half hour. We also set up several satellite offices as we expanded into other Hudson Valley counties. We were on a roll.

After separating from Eduardo, I never brought up the topic of divorce, knowing it would result in more bitterness and conflict. I hoped that one day, most likely because he'd want to remarry, he would be the one to initiate the formality. And that's what happened, sometime in 1994; I don't even remember the date. We never formalized any arrangements regarding custody, visitation, or child support and those things continued as before—haphazardly.

Mostly, I was happy, though. I was engaged in my work, and in being a single mother to an interesting and enjoyable adolescent son.

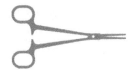

Chapter Twenty-Eight
TRIUMPHS AND TRAVESTIES

Remember that I never imagined myself doing anything business-related. In fact, in my family, becoming a business executive was as unthinkable as majoring in geology at Barnard! I used to tell people, "When I was in college or even in graduate school in public health, had anyone suggested that one day I'd work for an insurance company, I would have thrown up or punched them out." But Medicaid managed care was a new field, and its promise of health equity appealed to my sense of justice.

The early days of the enterprise were all about mission. It soon became clear, though, that ideology wasn't enough. Rather, I was stuck with a business model that seriously mitigated against the chances that the managed care enterprise would ever result in real reform. It wasn't just my own naiveté. When the original contracts were negotiated between the health plan and the community health centers, neither the regulators and policymakers in the state department of health, nor the leaders of the newly created HMOs, the physicians, nor the health centers themselves had a clue about how it would all work.

Nobody but nobody really knew how much it should cost to deliver high quality, equitable medical services to an underserved population.

And to this day, most medical care being provided does nothing to improve the health status of people who are economically and socially marginalized. Thus, most of the financial models the system relied upon were unproven at best.

Additionally, into the 1990s, because publicly funded managed care was outside the traditional, corporate insurance industry, many of the players were novices. They (no, *we*) had little experience in ramping up, funding reserves, and developing formulas and methods of data analysis and payment, and no expertise in training providers in new care and referral models—in short, all the things needed for long-term success. Compounding these problems, many of the players on the provider side expected some kind of short-term windfall, thinking that there was so much money floating around the health care system that being connected to an insurance company (as founders or through governance) was the ticket to raking it in.

Most of the leaders in this new type of health insurance came not from business school or the corporate world, but from the fields of social work, nursing, or public health. Further, most of us were women or minorities who were mission-driven, and recognized the opportunity to create rational models of financing and new service models that could help people who had never had the benefit of comprehensive, culturally sensitive primary and preventive health care.

As the health insurance world began to recognize Medicaid managed care as a serious business, though, more men, especially traditional white "businessmen," began to pursue the new positions opening up. But it was women and minorities who had set the course and piloted the Medicaid ship. In the chaotic world of managed health care for low-income people, women led the Armada.

Although my entry into a business leadership role was unexpected, I had always loved being around and working with people from different backgrounds. At Hudson Health Plan, after a few stumbles I embraced the freedom to hire the people I believed would contribute to a motivated, diverse, and creative team. My management style combined making my opinions and desires known while listening to everyone (and anyone, which sometimes caused problems); encouraging collaboration; and rewarding people who did a great job. Unlike some of my CEO colleagues in other health care organizations, I didn't insist on being front and center for every meeting, every event, every award. Over the years, my staff—many who like me had been business novices—came up through the company, taking advantage of our liberal tuition-reimbursement policies to get their undergrad and master's degrees. The environment was ripe for creating new models and programs and for sharing ideas with colleagues from other growing organizations.

It is a testament to Hudson's success that some of the people I brought in during the early 1990s stayed with me for twenty-plus years, developed award-winning programs, and became recognized leaders and executives in their fields. I also formed long-term relationships with many talented outside consultants who taught me a great deal and helped me and the organization grow and thrive.

In terms of the general health care system, though, during my twenty-five years in Medicaid managed care, as the business grew, so did my outrage. What had started as a mission to ensure equitable access to needed services gradually became a massive bureaucracy that supports the status quo. Who was serving whom?

And while insurance companies shamelessly deny needed prescriptions and procedures, they also pay for utterly unnecessary services, often to appease and retain doctors in their networks. Look no further than the penis business. Despite the government's prohibitions against using taxpayer dollars for medically unnecessary services, Medicaid pays for circumcision in almost every state. In states that do not cover circumcision, the managed care plans often pay for it anyway.

It was a source of constant mortification to me that Hudson Health Plan was obligated to pay for circumcision because it was a covered "benefit" under New York's Medicaid program. To mitigate this absurdity, we sent out regular communications to our pregnant members and in our newsletters, clearly stating that circumcision is not a necessary medical procedure, that it is painful and carries short- and long-term risks, and that it permanently alters a boy's genitals. I never felt that was enough.

I used to say that Medicaid managed care was the Wild West of American health care. Those of us in early leadership positions were empowered by a regulatory structure that had yet to harden into a rigid bureaucracy and—in many cases—by our own personalities and ambitions, to create new structures that would "make a difference." But I always knew that reforming the American health care system would require massive structural and financial changes and the collective will to dismantle the power of corporate interests—all unlikely to take place any time soon. Thankfully, though, I saw opportunities for changing certain practices that would improve the lives of, not just "patients," but those who worked in the health care system. What I learned starting up and running a health plan would prove invaluable to me when, a decade later, I began to focus in a systematic way on the problem of routine infant circumcision.

PART FOUR: BECOMING AN INTACTIVIST

Chapter Twenty-Nine
LAW SCHOOL?

When you're working a full-time job and decide to go to law school, your options are limited. Part-time evening programs are four years in duration (as opposed to three years for full-time day students). You have to find a place close enough to your home and work, because you'll be adding another commute and another three to five hours (not including study time) to your workday. Minimizing travel time is critical.

I didn't put much thought into the decision to apply to law school. I had run for mayor, a part-time office in the small village where I lived, in spring 1999. My partners in that effort were two neighbors, Fred Shaw and Lucie Saunders, both retired college professors. (Lucie was the person who later asked me how I got into "this penis business.") Thankfully, for me at least, we lost the election. My lofty ideas about preserving green space and limiting mega-mansions morphed into rumors that I planned to seize private property. I was also falsely accused of leaking to the press the recently discovered blooper that the Village's fancy new firetruck on order was too long to fit into the historic landmark firehouse. By the time the election took place, I knew that being mayor would result in nothing but headaches, for me and everyone else in the local government.

A few days after celebrating my loss as I was sitting at my desk at Hudson Health Plan, the thought of law school just popped into my mind. Many of my friends and colleagues, including Ernesto's "aunt" Barbara and Irene Dillon, whom I'd hired as legal counsel for the health plan, were attorneys. I loved the way they thought, the way they wrote, the way they approached problems. Becoming a lawyer myself had never crossed my mind.

But as my restless run for mayor probably suggests, I was looking for something more to do. I loved my job, my home, and my co-workers, and had turned away inquiries from a handful of recruiters looking to place me in another executive managed care position. My son was nearly twenty, bouncing around the Northeast among bicycle and snowboard shops, ski slopes and community colleges, and I felt a call to expand my horizons without turning my entire life upside down.

My only practical option for school was Pace University Law School, just 10 minutes from my Hudson Health Plan office. When I called Pace in early April to ask if they might still have openings in the Fall 1999 evening program and they said yes, it seemed like a good omen. I filled out an application and registered for the next Law School Admission Test (LSAT), scheduled several weeks hence. In the meantime, I received a provisional acceptance from Pace, contingent on my LSAT results; it would be my first standardized test in nearly 30 years.

I was in Honolulu when my LSAT score came in and—considering I'd barely had time to look at the review materials—I was relieved that it seemed good enough to get me in. Shortly thereafter Pace sent me an acceptance letter.

The only person happier than me about my going to law school was my mother. She had never gotten over her disappointment over me leaving grad school after getting my master's and passing my oral exams without finishing my PhD. After putting her own graduate work on hold for years, she had enrolled in an English literature program at Ohio State when my sister and I were in high school and our brothers were in elementary school, and she received her doctorate from Ohio State during my first year at Barnard. Her reminders that it was never too late to go back and finish were not as frequent as her remarks about my weight, but they were frequent enough. I didn't hold it against her (the PhD stuff, that is; the weight comments annoyed me no end), but neither did I feel like braving the research and dissertation-writing gauntlet. I am a terrible procrastinator—a college friend dubbed me "the Queen of Incompletes"—and I needed a straight, time-limited path if I was going to pursue another advanced degree. Someone had told me that incompletes were a no-no in law school. That turned out not to be true, but the misinformation bolstered my impression that law school would improve my moral character—at least with regard to procrastination.

When I started at Pace Law School in the fall of 1999, many friends and colleagues asked me "Why?" I wasn't looking for a new career. I didn't intend to open a law practice, so why go through all this? My response was always the same: *I just want to do it, and I can, so I will. Something will come of it. A new door will open.*

I'd heard from my lawyer friends that having a small and close-knit group of classmates to study with had greatly contributed to their well-being while in law school. From Day One at Pace, I immediately started scoping out members of the entering evening class. At 48, I had assumed I'd be the oldest among them, but that wasn't the case. In the first two days, I met Richard Agins, who was a CPA and at least five years older than me, and Cynthia Pittson, a librarian who worked for a commercial publisher and was a couple of years my junior. We three decided to band together. Over the next week, sitting in the cafeteria before classes started at six o'clock, I began courting another oldster (he was forty-five or so), Bob Schwartz, who had a PhD in hematology and was aiming to practice patent law. Bob was skeptical (true to his nature, as we were to see over time), and finally I had to tell him, "Look, we're all old and we're all smart; just join us," and he agreed. We began meeting every Sunday afternoon in my office at Hudson Health Plan, where we had plenty of coffee, lots of room to spread out our books and papers, and access to a good printer and copier. We took all the same classes the first year: Torts, Constitutional Law, Criminal Law, and Contracts. As time went on, we took fewer classes together but still met to study and hang out socially. These new friends were to be my core source of support for the next four years, and we kept in touch for years thereafter.

It didn't take me long to realize that I was in the right place to explore the topic that had been brewing in my brain for decades, and that had begun to niggle me in new ways since my son thanked me for not allowing him to be circumcised. Torts comprised personal injury law (including medical malpractice and violations of informed consent). Constitutional law was the basis for historical and contemporary legal struggles around individual rights, including privacy and bodily autonomy. The fact that U.S. doctors were not being prosecuted for surgically mutilating little boys' genitals, while they could be prosecuted for doing the same to little girls, implicated the *elements* of criminal law, if not its application in modern-day America.

As I got deeper into the law school curriculum, the analysis only got richer. Women refugees could apply for asylum based on their fear of being genitally mutilated in their home countries, but no man could dream of such a recourse. International Human Rights documents were crystal clear on individuals' rights to bodily autonomy and freedom from torture. And in the second semester of Health Law, most of the curriculum was devoted to bioethics, a body of laws and principles that govern the relationship between doctors and patients.

I also found a new a popular history of circumcision, published in 2000 by American journalist David Gollaher. Both serious and engaging, *Circumcision: A History of the World's Most Controversial Surgery* reflects the author's encyclopedic knowledge of the topic, past and present, religious and secular, and how it became intertwined with Western medicine. Not shirking the horror stories, but with humor, irony, and incredulity at the practice's tenacity, Gollaher also charted the progress of the small but serious movement afoot against infant circumcision in the United States.

That's when I hit my stride, writing (for my class in bioethics and medical malpractice) a comprehensive legal analysis and critique of the most common, and utterly unnecessary, pediatric surgery in the United States—routine infant male circumcision. At the end of the semester, each of us seven students presented our topics to the group and, from the start, I could feel mine making a huge impression. Tara, who worked in long-term care and was the mother of two daughters, said, "I am so relieved I have girls; I probably would not have known enough to say no." Chris, a hospital administrator, slumped in his chair and said, "I'm leaving here to yell at my mother and apologize to my son." Jay, who was in his mid-twenties, was incredulous and shell-shocked; he shook his head in wonderment, saying, "...my parents were hippies, and they still let this happen to me." The professor teaching the class, a Sephardic Jew, was shaken, and later very supportive of my work.

By that point, I was overwhelmed both with what I'd learned while writing the paper and with the enormous implications of what I was discovering, including (thanks to Gollaher) the fact that *there was a movement against infant circumcision!* There were people who thought like I did—that the routine circumcision of baby boys was one of the most important human rights causes of the (by then) 21ˢᵗ century! My next step was to get to know them.

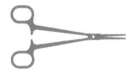

Chapter Thirty

THE TITANS OF INTACTIVISM

By the time this book is published, it will be more than sixty years since I witnessed my baby brother Chip's bloody circumcision wound; six decades since seeing the panic of my parents when a few days after bringing him home he had to be rushed to the doctor because he couldn't urinate. While I had no words at that time to name what happened to him, I knew if I was terrified by what I saw and felt, it must have been far worse for him. That feeling of "something terrible has happened" was always with me when I thought about Chip.

When I was in my early 20s and studying anthropology, I started speaking out. At the age of 28, I gave birth to a son, and keeping him intact was as much of a no-brainer as allowing him to keep all his fingers and toes.

Along the way, I had a few friends who agreed with me—including my college buddy Rachel who is Jewish, and her Christian (Greek Orthodox) husband. Outspoken and iconoclastic, Rachel was instinctively opposed to circumcision, but during her three pregnancies she lived in fear of her parents' disapproval should she have a son and forgo the obligatory *bris*.

"I just don't know how my mother would handle it," she'd say, "having a grandson who isn't circumcised." My atheist husband Eduardo knew about her dilemma and said the fact she ultimately gave birth to three daughters (thus avoiding the problem) proved there was a God.

In 2003, during my last semester in law school, I met my first real-life intactivists. My son was attending Fairhaven College's law and diversity program at Western Washington University, and my sister also lived in Bellingham, so I made a lot of weekend trips to Seattle and points north. On one of those trips, I decided to try for a meeting with John Geisheker, a New Zealand-born attorney who was (and still is) executive director of Doctors Opposing Circumcision (DOC). I sent John an email telling him that I ran a nonprofit HMO in New York State, that I had a long-standing interest in infant circumcision, and that, mid-career, I'd gone to law school and ended up devoting considerable time to the subject. I also told him I had a lot to learn, and that I wanted to join the movement. John wrote back right away and invited me to come and meet with him and George Denniston, the physician founder of DOC. We got together in the Capitol Hill apartment John shared with his wife Michaelle, an oncology nurse at a large Seattle medical center. John and George were both working for DOC as volunteers. Michaelle had committed to earning their household income so John could run DOC.

It's hard to convey the excitement—indeed the awe—I felt when I met John and George. There's a phrase in Spanish *"tocar el cielo con las manos."* I felt I'd touched the sky with my bare hands—that something extremely significant was happening in my life—that my stock answer (*Something will come up*) to the *Why law school?* question was now taking shape. These guys, like me, looked regular. But they were not. They, like me, were absorbed by a travesty that happened thousands of times every day in American hospitals but that few Americans were consciously aware of, and way fewer were able or willing to talk about. These guys, and the movement they represented, were fighting to end infant circumcision not just because the surgery was an unnecessary medical procedure, but because child genital mutilation was a massive social and human rights problem. As I talked with them, I began to feel that if I put my background and skills and my mind and energies to the task, *I could make a difference.*

Despite the years I'd been aware of the circumcision problem, I felt like a novice. But from the beginning John and George graciously welcomed me into their inner circle. A meeting was upcoming in April 2003 in Washington, D.C., to commemorate "Genital Integrity Awareness Week." Marilyn Milos, who I knew people revered as the "mother of the intactivist movement," would be there, along with other anti-circumcision activists (the term "intactivist" wasn't yet being widely used). Not only did they invite me to the meeting, but George offered me his speaking slot.

What could I possibly tell these people about the penis business? I thought. They knew so much more than I did. And they'd been working on it for years. But, of course, I agreed to go. I'd talk about a topic I *did* know something about: circumcision reimbursement under state Medicaid programs.

For the trip from Tarrytown to Washington, D.C., I recruited two companions—Irene Dillon, my close friend who served as legal counsel at Hudson Health Plan, and Dr. Carolyn Leihbacher, one of our medical directors. Both were mildly interested in the topic that had begun to obsess me and were curious to see what I was getting myself into.

After a five-hour drive south on Interstate 95, we ended up at a down-at-the-heels motor lodge in a scary part of D.C, within spitting distance from the Capitol. Once inside, it didn't feel scary, but it surely was different from any other gathering I'd ever attended—except maybe one of those weird international folkdance evenings from my past. Everyone had a name tag, and by then I was able to recognize some of them, chief among them Marilyn, a nurse and founder of the National Organization of Circumcision Information Resource Centers (NOCIRC). Marilyn greeted me with great enthusiasm, saying George had told her about me. Then she excused herself to disappear upstairs where a woman named Amanda was in labor and Marilyn was monitoring her progress.

John Geisheker introduced me to those in the conference room. I met a lawyer named Steven Svoboda (founder and director of Attorneys for the Rights of the Child and a Harvard Law School classmate of Barack Obama); Dan Bollinger (an industrial designer, now vice-chair of Intact America); an ex-Mormon housepainter from Utah named Steve Scott; David Wilson, a Florida man with long blond dreadlocks who made his living mowing lawns; Amber Craig, an intense North Carolina mom with butterscotch-colored hair who was working with Dan and others on a Medicaid circumcision-defunding project; and William Stowell, a young man recently discharged from the military who had sued the hospital where he was born because his mother had been pressured into signing a consent for his circumcision while she was under the influence of drugs administered during his birth. (William's wife was Amanda, the person who was in labor one floor up from the meeting.)

As Amber stood to speak, I was still surveying the room in wonderment at this improbable collection of humanity. I remember her saying, perhaps by way of introducing the movement to me, "There's probably only one thing everyone in this room agrees on: that people should stop cutting off little boys' foreskins." Never religious, for me that was an "amen" moment.

Chapter Thirty-One

PROFESSIONAL INTACTIVIST IN TRAINING

Three months after my first intactivist gathering, I graduated from Pace University School of Law. Sonia Sotomayor, who was to become a United States Supreme Court Justice, was our commencement speaker. No graduation ceremony had ever meant so much to me. I overflowed with good will and gratitude for Pace's evening program so near to my office and home; for the diverse and stimulating faculty; for my fellow evening student classmates, nearly all who held other full-time jobs and many who also were parenting young children; and for my coworkers and executive team who ensured that Hudson Health Plan continued to thrive even as I arrived bleary-eyed every morning from class and studying the previous night.

My parents in Honolulu were thrilled but didn't make it to my graduation. Instead, they sent a chilled box that contained a gorgeous fresh orchid and ginger flower lei to wear over my graduation gown. And they sent me a wood-block print by Hawaiian artist Dietrich Varez of Lauhiamanuikahiki, daughter of Hina, the goddess Pele's sister, swimming with a turtle. They attached notes to the back of the framed print. My mother's note told me the legend of Lauhiamanuikahiki being rescued from captivity and returning to her first love in Kauai. Hank told me the print was called, "Woman Conquers Law School."

A new door had opened, and now I was going to have more time on my hands, so to speak, for the penis business. I decided to defer taking the bar exam until the following winter, and to take a breather over the sweet summer and fall months.

After four years of being busy round-the-clock with school and work, I began to see friends and travel again, making regular trips to visit my son and my sister's family in Washington state; to California to spend time with Marilyn Milos and my cousin Paula; and to Hawaii, where my mother was beginning to show signs of the health problems that would eventually take away her mind and her spirit.

As if my mother's decline wasn't enough, my brother Chip's mental and physical health also were deteriorating. On one of my trips to Honolulu, Hank asked me not to talk about circumcision around Chip, then in his mid-40s, because "he doesn't like being circumcised."

This was the first time I heard that the subject had been raised in the household, perhaps as part of a conversation about my growing involvement in intactivism. As Hank requested, I never spoke of circumcision again in front of Chip, and he never asked me about it. I was still processing my personal and emotional relationship with the issue, and I assumed a conversation would have been awkward and painful for both of us. Although Chip's circumcision experience had affected me greatly, I never talked with my parents or Chip about it, except for the brief conversation when Hank told me he and my mom hadn't been asked: "They just did it," he said.

Chip's struggles with mental illness were evident to me beginning when he was a young child. However, not until I became involved in the intactivist movement and began hearing the stories of other men who had been circumcised as newborns and had experienced flashbacks, recurring night terrors, and obsessive thoughts about hurting themselves did I come to believe that Chip's mental illness could be related – at least in part—to his two penis surgeries during his first week of life. In addition to the personal accounts I was hearing from survivors, the growing body of scholarship on the long-term effects of early trauma and Adverse Childhood Experiences (ACEs) supports the position that child genital cutting qualifies as an ACE.[7]

Somehow, despite work and travel and my growing involvement in the penis business, I managed to study for—and even pass—the New York bar exam. My parents had a hand in that, too. The front entrance of the Manoa Animal Hospital, just a few blocks from their Honolulu home, was graced with a bronze statue of a big dachshund that had belonged to one of the veterinarians. In addition to my mixed-breed Benji-esque terrier Julio, I owned a very large, very mean, black and tan dachshund named Huckleberry, whom Ernesto and I dearly loved. The Manoa dachshund reminded my family and me of Huck, except that, because the former was a statue, no one had to worry that it would attack a passerby. On the eve of the first day of the exam, my mom and Hank drove to the Manoa Animal Hospital and ceremonially draped several plumeria lei around the bronze dachshund's body and neck, as their way of conveying (from 5000 miles away) their wishes that I pass the exam. They then sent me an email telling me the ceremony had taken place.

Given my compulsive solitaire-playing during the time I was supposed to be studying and my jitters over the two-day exam, the only plausible explanation for my passing the first time around was that lei-draped bronze dachshund, my ʻaumākua (guardian). I still have the coffee mug with the photo commemorating my parents' final contribution to me becoming a lawyer.

I was admitted to the bar in the summer of 2004. Shortly thereafter, I accepted an invitation from Pace Law School to become an adjunct faculty member. First I taught a course in Medicaid and Disability Law and then the school's second-semester health law course in Bioethics and Medical Malpractice.

For the former, I assigned an exercise that required the students to navigate the enormous and mystifying bureaucracy of applying and qualifying for Medicaid and disability benefits. For the latter, I built a three-week mini-course about infant circumcision, the peculiar American custom that served as a spectacular case study of cognitive dissonance, medical fraud, and ethical bankruptcy in American medicine. Circumcision as a bioethical case study gave me the opportunity to walk a group of twenty law students through an almost embarrassingly simple analysis, showing that routine child genital cutting (aka circumcision) violates every principle of bioethics, a set of philosophical and practical guidelines largely developed after World War II in response to atrocities committed by Nazi doctors upon Jews and other marginalized peoples. Here is a very brief discussion of those principles.[8]

Autonomy (and its associated mandate of informed consent). This principle holds that only the individual who will be at risk for the consequences of a medical intervention has the right to make a decision as to whether to undergo that intervention. Clearly, no child has the capacity to make such a decision; indeed, babies loudly protest the removal of their foreskins. "Proxy" (e.g., parental) consent is permitted only in cases where the child's life or health are at risk. A normal foreskin does not require removal; indeed, its removal serves no therapeutic purpose. Therefore, routine circumcision violates the principle of autonomy.

Non-maleficence (the principle underlying the precept "do no harm"). While discussions of benefit and harm can get complicated, forcibly removing a child's foreskin clearly infringes on their rights to their body as property and their expectations to be free from a violation that causes pain and suffering.

Beneficence (the obligation to perform acts of kindness and mercy and to confer benefit to the patient). Amputating a child's foreskin is a cruel act that confers no benefit to the child. Therefore, male child genital cutting violates the bioethical principle of beneficence.

Justice (treating patients fairly). Male child genital cutting inflicts needless injury on the child, violating his rights to bodily integrity. Also, it discriminates against males, given that only female children are protected by U.S. law from non-therapeutic genital cutting. This violates the bioethical principle of justice.

Teaching law school was fun—thrilling, actually. The evening students were as motivated as I had been just a few years earlier when I enrolled in that program and seemed truly grateful (as I also had been) to explore new themes, new bodies of knowledge, and new ways of seeing the world. The problem for me, though, was that I was too busy; teaching one class demanded as much or more preparation than taking two classes myself. Plus, I had to be "on," talking or leading the discussion for an entire two hours in the evening, twice a week. So, after two semesters,

I retreated to my "normal" life—running a company with 350 employees and ramping up my intactivism.

I was able to manage all of this—law school, a heavy-duty job, maintaining contact with my family 5000 miles away, and my growing commitment to figuring out how to torpedo the penis business—because I had the most wonderful group of colleagues on my executive team at work. And at home I had an amazing live-in boyfriend (I'll call him D) who took care of the house and the pets while I did my thing. D was a Jamaican-born contractor I'd met several years earlier when I was shopping for some repairs on a rental property I owned. We'd become friendly, and a couple of years later, after putting a new roof on my house, he moved in. The relationship provoked considerable curiosity among some of my acquaintances, if for no other reason than that D was seventeen years younger than me. But most of my close friends were accustomed to a certain lack of orthodoxy in my choices, and they recognized that he was kind and generous, that we were similarly independent, and that the relationship worked.

Crucially, D was supportive—indeed, proud—of my growing involvement in intactivism. He had a young daughter and told me that when her mother was pregnant, circumcision had been a huge point of disagreement. He insisted that if the child was a boy he should NOT be cut, and she taunted him by saying she had money put aside for the surgery because no baby of hers was going to have an "un-American dick." She, too, had been born in Jamaica, but had come to the United States as a young child and seemed to have internalized the mainstream American idea that foreskins are repugnant. D told me many times how grateful he had been when the baby, his only child, turned out to be a girl. His relationship with her mother ended shortly thereafter.

Women executives know how unusual it is to find a male partner whose ego is sufficiently intact to not feel threatened by a woman who is financially independent and busy outside the home. D was such a man. D also was the first person to tell me about an experience I learned later was all too common among men in the United States whose penises had not been surgically reduced. Sometime before we met, he had landed in an emergency room with chest pains following a minor car crash. The ER doctor examining him noted his intact penis, and commented, "You can get that fixed, you know?" gesturing toward D's foreskin. "It's only going to cause you trouble."

I've heard numerous similar stories involving boys and men of all ages.

I began spending more and more time on intactivism. I attended several of the symposia convened by Marilyn Milos of NOCIRC (later re-named Genital Autonomy-America). I wrote essays and articles, some for the symposia, and others that simply helped me to expand my knowledge and my analysis. Over time, the people I met who were working on ending circumcision and recognizing the rights of infants and children to their own bodies became my sounding board and my good friends.

A couple of years after I become involved in the movement, John Geisheker and I were chatting about how we couldn't help ourselves from voicing our outrage about the blasé acceptance of male child genital cutting. Even a random, seemingly unrelated topic, we agreed, could immediately provoke us into a diatribe. John asked me: "Has it happened yet that no one is inviting you to parties anymore?"

"Yes!" I exclaimed. "I thought it was my imagination!"

Even my friends were looking away nervously when I describe the mechanics of a circumcision—how the doctor swabs the immobilized baby, pries his foreskin from the head of the penis with a metal probe, clamps the foreskin for several minutes to keep it from bleeding, and then cuts away between half and two-thirds of the penile skin. "And during the whole thing, the baby is shrieking until he passes out in shock."

Hmm. No wonder people look away, I thought to myself. *Who wants to hear that?*

The fact that I've never shied away from an unpopular cause that I believe in is beside the point. In general, this is true. But with a topic as loaded as circumcision, I was beginning to understand that if I wanted people to consider my viewpoint, I needed to present it in a way that didn't make them profoundly uncomfortable from the moment I opened my mouth. Too much information for someone new to a disturbing issue—one they've never considered—is a real risk.

Fortunately, not just for my social calendar, but for the success of our movement, I've toned down my approach. I've found that the most effective way to bring up the issue is to tell my own personal stories: how I witnessed the traumatic results from the circumcision of a baby in my family, and how over the years many men and women have told me how their intimate relationships and lives have been harmed by the after-effects of male genital cutting.

I might share that I've observed that the medical industry undermines the instincts of parents (mothers, especially) to protect their new-born babies. But I no longer launch into graphic details right away. I have learned it is more productive to allow my companion to listen without feeling assaulted and to go away to ponder the conversation without any pressure to react or to respond.

Chapter Thirty-Two

FOUNDING INTACT AMERICA

s I got to know Marilyn Milos better, I began to hear the name Dean Pisani a lot. Dean had been donating to NOCIRC since the birth of his first child, a son. He told Marilyn that during a visit to his wife's obstetrician, the doctor (a woman) asked them casually, "If it's a boy, you're going to circumcise him, right?"

When Dean asked the doctor why they might want to do that, she answered, "Because everyone does."

That made Dean bristle. He later told me he'd responded, "What is this? Junior high school? We're supposed to circumcise our baby because everybody does that?"

Dean and his wife kept their son intact.

"I call him when I need funds for the *American Baby* magazine ad," Marilyn explained. "Or a one-time expenditure I can't otherwise meet. But he told me that one day he wanted to do something big for the movement."

Dean obviously understood the issue, but I didn't spend any time wondering what he might have in mind for helping the movement. Intrigued by the many passionate and diverse people I was meeting, I was content to watch and learn while they took care of business.

My day job required a lot of time and energy. Since I'd become CEO fifteen years earlier, Hudson Health Plan had grown from a start-up to a full-blown insurance company with nearly 350 employees. We now occupied two floors of the building overlooking the Hudson River in Tarrytown where we'd moved in 1993, as well as several satellite offices throughout the Hudson Valley. Also, in 2004, the same year I was admitted to the New York bar, I'd started up a new nonprofit called the Hudson Center for Health Equity and Quality, a hybrid advocacy and technology company. Together with members of the health plan's executive team, I hired a social entrepreneurship consulting firm called Pepin Tranquada (later renamed Aperio) to assist with developing this new mission-focused, (hopefully) self-sustaining company.

The Hudson Center's initial project was to create New York's first electronic Medicaid application, designed to cut down the time it took for eligible individuals to get onto the Medicaid rolls. The old system we were hoping to replace required uninsured people, many who urgently needed medical services, to wait for months to get an insurance card and see a doctor. The Hudson Center's enrollment tool cut that wait down to days, or a couple of weeks, at most. The success of that effort led us to explore other ways to streamline administrative processes that disproportionately burdened people who relied on the social safety net for their health care. The Hudson Center's tagline was "Creating a humane, cost-effective, high quality health care system for all stakeholders."

Meanwhile, I was becoming more deeply involved in intactivism. In early 2007, at Marilyn's invitation, I attended a meeting in San Francisco led by a consultant from an organization called SmartMeme, later renamed the Center for Story-Based Strategy. SmartMeme had been suggested by Joan and Mark Reiss as a company that could help us develop a strategic narrative for the movement. Joan worked for a breast cancer research organization. Mark, a retired Jewish radiologist and a concert pianist, had experienced a traumatic flashback to his *bris* (ritual circumcision) during a massage. He then began advocating against all infant circumcision – religious and medical. Mark would later become an officiant at *brit shalom* (peaceful *bris*, or *bris* without cutting) ceremonies around the world.[9]

We all emerged from the SmartMeme meeting with far more questions than answers, and a conviction that the movement was crying out for strategy, leadership, and a unified message.

A couple of months later, Marilyn called to tell me Dean Pisani was ready to step up his support. He asked her to think about how to build the movement into something more powerful. In response, she was pulling together the leaders and founders of four organizations—NOCIRC (Marilyn), Doctors Opposing Circumcision (attorney John Geisheker). Attorneys for the Rights of the Child (attorney Steven Svoboda), and the International Coalition for Genital Integrity (industrial designer Dan Bollinger). She also was inviting a few other people with a history in the movement whom she thought could be helpful, and asked if I would join a conference call with Dean.

I don't remember many details from the call, only that it quickly became clear the group was going to need some outside help articulating our goals and organizing the next steps. I thought about the social entrepreneurship consultants who helped me start the Hudson Center and offered to reach out and ask if they'd be interested in working with "us." Note how quickly I went from being a participant observer to being part of the movement! Everyone on the call seemed relieved that at least we had a next step.

Dean gave me the go-ahead to have that conversation. He said that if he felt comfortable with the consultants, and upon my recommendation, he'd fund the exploratory effort. I contacted Warren Tranquada from Aperio and, within a couple of weeks, we had a preliminary proposal for the consulting engagement. To the consultants' budget, I added the cost of bringing the core group of participants together, because most of them would not be able to afford the costs of travel and lodging. Dean approved it.

The first in-person meeting took place in the corporate office of Dean's company, an environmental remediation firm located a short distance from the Dallas airport. The firm was like no corporate office I'd seen before, minimalist and modern, with polished concrete floors and a lot of stainless steel. In the middle of the space was a conference room and a kitchen stocked with healthy snacks and drinks. Behind the kitchen was an open exercise room with a treadmill, weight-training equipment, and floor-to-ceiling windows to the outside.

Staff members' offices were located around most of the perimeter. Remarkably, I noted that every office—Dean's included—was the same size. No big corner suite for the CEO. The staff, mostly engineers, were friendly enough. They must have been wondering why Dean (dressed in spiffy jeans) was spending his day in the conference room with this rag-tag bunch of visitors.

Most of the people at the table that day had been working against infant circumcision for years, if not decades. We spent considerable time talking about our dreams for the future—lawsuits, a ban on Medicaid payments for circumcisions, legislation prohibiting the cutting of minors, and so on. Warren and John Baker, the consultants, mostly listened. They then proposed interviewing not just the individuals in the room that day, but a larger group of intactivists (recommended by those of us at the meeting), to elicit their vision for the movement's future.

We set a date for a second Dallas meeting, and the consultants went to work. When we gathered again, they presented their data about insiders' perceptions of the movement and their collective agreement on the need for it to grow. They also recommended that, because none of the existing entities had the infrastructure upon which to build or to execute a merger, we needed a new organization.

When no one objected, Warren said, "Let's talk about the name."

I remember thinking, *Well, this will take a while.*

But then Dan offered: "How about Intact America?"

We looked around the table at each other. Yes! It sounded good; we agreed.

In the meantime, Warren and I talked about leadership. I loved the people who had done the work over the previous 25 years. But I also saw that no one was stepping up to the task of leading a more robust organization with a professional staff, sophisticated fundraising capability, a public relations firm on retainer—in short, all the things required for a successful national human rights organization. On one hand, the realization overwhelmed me. On the other hand, I had begun to envision a fascinating new opportunity. I offered to host the next meeting in my office in Tarrytown, New York. On the agenda was a presentation by the consultants to the group—and most importantly to Dean—about budget and growth projections for the new, as-yet leaderless, organization.

We met in Hudson Health Plan's executive conference room. It was decorated with framed ethnic posters I'd selected over the years to reflect the diversity of our staff and the people we served. Before starting the meeting, I gave a tour to Dean and other members of the planning group. Hudson Health Plan's large bilingual member services department particularly impressed them—that along with how friendly our staff was to visitors.

When the meeting began, I was sitting across the glass-topped table from Dean, Marilyn, and Dan. Warren was on my right with a laser pointer, and John was at the other end making real-time adjustments to the presentation on the screen. Sitting to my left were Amber Craig, Steven Svoboda, and John Geisheker. As Warren walked through the budget presentation—$140,000 the first year, $175,000 the second year—I could see Dean, leaning sideways in his chair and shaking his head.

"No." he interjected. looking at me. "I want to know what we can do with a million dollars." He looked at me. "Can you do this?"

Marilyn gasped, her tears actually shooting across the table.

Dan jumped in: "Georganne, do it for six months, then we can bring in someone else to replace you."

Nobody objected.

Years later, Dan told me that he, Warren, and Dean had huddled privately during the second Dallas meeting, when it had become obvious that we needed to start a new organization. Dean expressed his vote of confidence in my leadership, but Dan saw my reluctance to step up because I had so many other things on my plate. That's when they decided to propose that I take the job temporarily, while a search was conducted for a permanent executive director. They hadn't included me in that discussion.

When Dean asked me, and Marilyn started weeping, I knew resistance was futile.

"I guess it's my calling," I said later that day to Marilyn, also thanking her for showing me what the phrase "projectile tears" meant.

"Exactly!" she replied. "I had my eye on you from the day I met you. It *is* your calling."

PART FIVE:
ACTION AND ACCOUNTABILITY

Chapter Thirty-Three

SMOKE AND MIRRORS, COURTESY OF THE AMERICAN ACADEMY OF PEDIATRICS

Approximately 1.4 million American baby boys lose their foreskins at the hands of medical professionals every year. Who bears the responsibility for this travesty?

When childbirth moved into the hospital, and obstetricians, rather than traditional birth attendants such as lay midwives, attended mothers during labor and delivery, the OB was the doctor who amputated the baby's foreskin. Over time, as medical specialization evolved, general practitioners (mostly replaced now by board-certified family physicians) also took care of pregnant mothers and delivered their babies, especially in areas where obstetricians were in short supply. These doctors also cut the babies.

Today, the person who circumcises a newborn baby boy in the hospital could be an obstetrician, family physician, nurse-midwife, pediatrician, urologist, medical resident—even a medical student. Some of the factors that influence who carries out the circumcisions in a given hospital or geographic area include the local physician labor force; where they trained; doctors' willingness (or lack thereof) to perform the procedure;

socioeconomic and racial disparities in patients' access to prenatal and other medical care; and other purely administrative vicissitudes, such as the division of labor in any given facility. I've spoken with many women who weren't sure of the specialty (or even the name) of the person who cut their son.

My pediatrician friend Ken Zatz tells me that when he was doing his residency "100 years ago" (he's in his sixties), "the culture was no pediatrician east of the Mississippi was trained to do them but every pediatrician in the west was." He said that these days around New York, it's mostly obstetricians and urologists, though he knows a pediatrician in a suburb north of New York City who trained in Texas and cuts babies in his office. Many large hospitals take a nearly assembly-line approach to foreskin removal, with one or two doctors assigned (or stepping up) to the task. My obstetrician friend Jim V (who refuses to do circumcisions) works in a San Francisco hospital that caters to affluent patients. Jim estimates that nearly three-quarters of the boys born in that facility leave without their foreskins. One of his enthusiastic colleagues does (and bills for) nearly all those circumcisions. "They line 'em up, and I go in there and just chop, chop, chop," he quoted her as saying recently. "It's all about the RVUs [Relative Value Units]."[10]

Just across the San Francisco Bay in Berkeley, obstetric nurse Tora Spigner reports, "In my hospital, it is pretty much only pediatricians doing it because the old school obstetricians (mostly men) are no longer there."[11]

No matter who cuts the baby, the American Academy of Pediatricians (AAP) is the organization that works the hardest to ensure the continuity of the practice of circumcision. It's the AAP that makes sure doctors get paid for doing circumcisions, and that protects them (as well as the trade association itself) from liability by shifting the burden of "deciding", and therefore the moral responsibility for the act, to parents. Founded in 1930, at the same time that private insurance was evolving as a business, the AAP's two-part mission statement is "to attain optimal physical, mental, and social health and well-being for all infants, children, adolescents and young adults," and to "support the professional needs of its members."

In fulfilling the first part of its mission, the AAP goes far afield of scientific medicine and public health principles, asserting its authority about a wide range of non-medical childrearing practices. Historically, most of these have been the purview of parents, extended family, and the larger community. But now, pediatricians have become "expert" advice-givers, the last word, on topics as varied as toilet training, breastfeeding, sibling rivalry, the effects on children's intellectual and language development in multilingual versus bilingual households, co-sleeping, and more recently "screen time." Such customs vary widely, and even conflict, within a diverse and heterogeneous society. To accommodate such diversity, the AAP's recommendations are often more confusing than helpful. Its position on circumcision is a stellar example of such confusion.

As for the second part of its mission (supporting members' "professional needs"), not surprisingly, ensuring doctors' income is a preeminent concern for the AAP. Over the decades, as the medical industry has grown into a massive money machine, the AAP has created the demand for the harmful and medically unnecessary removal of little boys' foreskins, assured parents (including, of course, grown men) that the procedure is benign, and worked to guarantee that doctors get paid for doing it.

The Academy's first official statement about infant male circumcision goes back to 1971 when it issued a report stating: "There are no valid medical indications for circumcision in the neonatal period."[12] This was a curiously unequivocal stance, given that at the time it was written few newborn boys were escaping American hospitals with their complete penises.

Perhaps this is why just four years later, the AAP's 1975 statement— while reaffirming the absence of medical reasons for circumcision—introduced among factors for parents to weigh a new, thinly veiled warning pertaining to boys who remained intact: "the necessity for lifelong penile hygiene." Implying that a normal foreskin required special care (a misconception that persists to this day) and hinting that circumcision would mean never having to wash "down there"), this cautionary aside armed doctors with an argument in favor of the cut.

Additionally, the 1975 statement was the first time the Academy gave a nod to non-medical justifications for neonatal circumcision by mentioning "traditional, cultural and religious factors" that parents might consider when deciding whether to cut their sons. Finally, the authors recommended that doctors "provide parents with factual and informative medical options," concluding, "The final decision is theirs, and should be based on true informed consent."

The AAP chose to reconfirm the 1975 statement in 1977, and in 1983, the American Congress of Obstetricians and Gynecologists signed on in support.[13]

At the same time, grassroots organizations were organizing letter-writing campaigns, public demonstrations, and the publication of first-person accounts from aggrieved men who felt permanently harmed by having their genitals cut as infants, and from aggrieved mothers who realized they had been lied to and coerced into allowing their sons to be circumcised.

Clearly sensing that doctors were on the ropes, the AAP formed a new Circumcision Task Force with outspoken pro-circumcision physician Edgar J. Schoen, Chief of Pediatrics at Kaiser Permanente in Sacramento, California, as Chair. The new report was released in 1989. Under Schoen's leadership, the new task force trivialized concerns about the value of the foreskin and the ethical violations implicated in removing an essential part of newborn boys' penises. In an obvious effort to protect both circumcisers and the trade association from liability, the report issued by Schoen's task force advised doctors to share with parents the so-called benefits and risks (the latter grossly unexplored and understated), in order to obtain "informed" consent. This emphasis on consent (raised for the first time in the prior report) was in response to growing awareness in the media and the public that the procedure was problematic, at best, and that this information was not being shared with parents.

This intentionally created confusion had the effect of shifting not just the decision whether to circumcise, but the consequences of the surgery itself, squarely onto the shoulders of parents. Mothers and fathers were now somehow supposed to sort through pages and pages of pseudoscientific and intentionally confusing information and assertions, and to decide whether foreskin amputation (though not recommended for "all boys") should be carried out on *their* boys.

This "guidance" was confirmed and amplified in the Task Force's next statement, published in 1999, where yet another vague and insidious concept was introduced. No longer led by Schoen (though he continued to espouse pro-circumcision views when interviewed by *The New York Times* about the report), the new task force declared: "In circumstances in which there are potential benefits and risks, yet the procedure is not essential to the child's current wellbeing, parents should determine what is in the best interest of the child...."[14] They didn't define "best interest" or provide any guidance as to how this might be calculated.

For the first time, though, likely in acknowledgment of established proof against the absurd myth that babies do not feel pain, the AAP recommended the use of "procedural analgesia" for neonatal circumcision. One could be forgiven for thinking that several decades of unanesthetized surgery, alone, had not been in any babies' best interest. Perhaps the authors of the new report hoped that temporary and partial pain relief would tip the scales in the other direction.

To keep the confusion alive, the AAP convened yet another task force in 2007. Headed by Susan Blank, a pediatrician who specialized in infectious disease, and with Douglas Diekema representing the AAP's Committee on Bioethics, the group began tackling the burgeoning literature coming from circumcision campaigns being conducted in sub-Saharan Africa in an effort to prove circumcision's efficacy in preventing transmission of HIV.

New and older academicians and career public health professionals, supported by massive amounts of money from the U.S. government and from the Clinton and Gates foundations, were making their reputations as researchers in campaigns designed to remove the foreskins of as many intact African males as possible. The stated hypothesis of the research was that mass circumcision would reduce the spread of HIV in sub-Saharan Africa. Activists like me knew the true purpose of these efforts was to promulgate male circumcision in countries that had never adopted the practice.

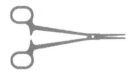

Chapter Thirty-Four

INTACT AMERICA BATTLES THE MEDICAL POWERS THAT BE

The days and months following the launch of Intact America in 2008 were filled with organizational tasks of hiring staff and consultants, discussing strategy with a multitude of stakeholders, creating a web and social media presence, and building a constituent database and fundraising plan. Intact America was developing tactics designed to change the way Americans think about circumcision, and—ultimately—to reach a tipping point where the majority of Americans would accept an intact penis as normal. We designed a beautiful trade show booth, with literature about Intact America and a separate standalone banner that listed "10 Reasons Not to Circumcise Baby Boys," and began registering for booths in the nonprofit section of the exhibit halls for the annual conferences of the American Academy of Pediatrics (AAP) and the American Association of Family Physicians (AAFP).

My colleagues and I knew about the new AAP Task Force on circumcision and that it was led by a specialist in infectious disease. We suspected the group was going to issue a report that might, for the first time, go so far as to recommend the practice, bolstered by the giddy claims being made about circumcision as an effective measure to reduce transmission of HIV. Intact America's next public foray, then, was to take a booth at the 2009 National HIV Prevention Conference, convened by the Centers for Disease Control at the Hyatt Regency Hotel in downtown Atlanta. While inside we handed out literature about the shameful way men were being pressured into "consenting" to the removal of their foreskins, outside a small truck wrapped with the Intact America logo and a message proclaiming "Tell the CDC that Circumcision Doesn't Prevent AIDS" circulated through the downtown streets surrounding the conference facility. We also ran an ad in *The Atlanta Journal-Constitution* and sent out a press release about our position and our attendance at the conference. Mike Stobbe, an Associated Press (AP) reporter, was the only person who showed up to interview me, and a small piece about Intact America ran in several newspapers.

The conference attendees included dozens of public health officials, academics, and entrepreneurs seeking to profit from the African "studies" and the business they would create. Among the latter were medical equipment manufacturers (selling newfangled devices of torture and single-use circumcision kits) and even an Israeli company called Operation Abraham, promoting its expertise in adult circumcision gained from circumcising new immigrants to that country. It is not an exaggeration to say that the atmosphere was one of evangelical fervor and self-congratulation, with presenters and audience members alike delighting at the prospect of a new, mass "public health" effort designed to separate millions of black men from their foreskins, in countries where vast sectors of the population had no running water or access to basic health care.

In these early days of Intact America, in addition to seeking out opportunities to showcase our new organization's principles, goals, and plans, we looked to both create and respond to events that featured the conflict and thus highlighted our work. Weeks might go by without even a single article about circumcision appearing in the mainstream press. Once in a while though, our antagonists handed us an opportunity on the proverbial silver platter.

As the AAP's Circumcision Task Force was working on its upcoming report, apparently unbeknownst to the organization's powers-that-be, another committee was working on a related issue —female genital cutting—and preparing to issue a recommendation.

On April 26, 2010, the journal *Pediatrics* published online a "Policy Statement on the Ritual Genital Cutting of Female Minors." That statement was prepared and authored by the Committee on Bioethics, chaired by none other than Douglas Diekema, with bioethicist Dena Davis acting as consultant. In it, the Committee reminded readers that the Academy's position on newborn male circumcision "acknowledges the legitimacy of including cultural, religious and ethnic traditions for parents considering whether to surgically alter a male infant's genitals." The authors also commented, "Some forms of [female genital cutting] are less extensive than the newborn male circumcision commonly performed in the West." They then put forth an astonishing proposal: namely, that American pediatricians be permitted to "offer" a "ritual nick" on the labia or clitorises of little girls. The committee acknowledged that such a practice would violate federal statute as well as many states' laws prohibiting all forms of medically unnecessary tampering with the genitalia of girls under the age of 18; these laws would have to be changed, they said. Continuing, the authors posited that allowing such a minor and "harmless" intervention would prevent parents from certain African countries from returning to their homelands to have their daughters cut more invasively.[15]

All hell broke loose, with human rights and women's organizations as well as the national media expressing outrage—and confusion. Intact America purchased a large ad in the first section of *The Washington Post* and published a letter demanding that the AAP immediately repudiate and withdraw its new Policy Statement.

An article in *The New York Times* quoted me saying I was "astonished that a group of intelligent people did not see the utter slippery slope that we put physicians on" with the new statement. The British medical journal *The Lancet* quoted Taina Bien Aimé, president of Equality Now, as calling all forms of female genital cutting "a whole package of abuse and denial of girls' rights."[16] Ironically, when I had reached out to Equality Now to propose issuing a joint statement denouncing the Bioethics Committee's report, I was rebuffed; this type of response from anti-FGM advocates who perceive that allying with the movement against male child circumcision undermines their own gains persists even to the present.

After initially denying that the statement said what it said, the AAP leadership buckled down to manage the fiasco. Dr. Judith Palfrey, at the time president of the organization, was quoted in a June 2, 2010, online article in the industry publication *Medscape.com* as saying the original comment about doctors performing a medically unnecessary nick represented an "academic discussion of options" and not a recommendation. "Obviously, having a discussion inside a policy statement is confusing. We regret this." She went on to say, "The ethics committee will do a rewrite, which will reassert the AAP opposition to all forms of female genital cutting."[17]

In the meantime, my insurance executive brain was spinning. I couldn't help thinking about the bureaucratic tasks—at once, mundane and horrifying—that would ensue from incorporating a "ritual" genital nick into mainstream pediatric medicine.

What would the diagnosis be? Presence of unwounded labia and clitoris?

Who would come up with the procedure and billing codes? Doug Diekema?

What would the intervention be called on a consent form or physician bill? Female circumcision?

Certainly, it would not be called "female genital mutilation." Probably not "ritual nick," either. "Routine neonatal male circumcision" in American hospitals and clinics is not called "ritual" anything. Rather, the act is cloaked in language that obfuscates its true nature, facilitating doctors' sales job and the transfer of money from the "payer" (parents, insurance companies, Medicaid) to the human and institutional parties who collude in the violation.

Finally, would the AAP lobby for Medicaid to cover female genital mutilation (oops, circumcision), just as they do for male genital mutilation?

Federal law prohibits the use of federal health care dollars for medically unnecessary services. Medicaid funding of routine infant circumcision clearly flies in the face of that prohibition, but the AAP has managed to obfuscate the practice's purely cultural origins (I include religion in the broad category of culture) by its serial quest to find medical benefits. Not so with FGM. It is heresy to even hint that the analogous removal of mucosal tissue from a girl's genitals might reduce her chances of acquiring one infection or another.

I also wondered who would train doctors how to perform a ritual nick (*would the AAP hire lay circumcisers from Muslim immigrant communities?*) and how much doctors could charge? Finally, I wondered whether work was underway already to convince insurance companies to add the ritual nick to their "benefit" package.

Even given the AAP's "no problem" attitude toward male circumcision, I was incredulous that the committee members themselves had failed to understand the magnitude of their "discussion." As for the trade association's powers-that-be, how could they have paid so little attention to the Bioethics Committee's work?

Or, I thought, maybe the whole thing wasn't such an anomaly. Maybe, as the AAP's circumcision task force was continuing its quest to maintain and even grow the American penis business, Diekema (who was on both the Bioethics Committee and the circumcision task force) and others had this thought: *What a great way to nullify the arguments about gender inequity: make male and female genital cutting "equal" and acceptable. And make sure that doctors can get paid for all of it!*

The fact that no one at the AAP appears to have taken the fall for the disastrous pro-ritual nick statement is supported by the fact that Doug Diekema lived on to further trivialize the harms of male child genital cutting as a co-author of the Academy's next (and longest ever) Task Force Report on Circumcision. This was the one we'd been waiting for, before being blindsided by the "FGM-lite" Bioethics Committee travesty.

In the report (published in the journal *Pediatrics* in September 2012),[18] the Circumcision Task Force got straight to business, with the second paragraph of the abstract and the first recommendation in the body of the report reading: "Evaluation of current evidence indicates that the health benefits of newborn male circumcision outweigh the risks; furthermore, the benefits of newborn male circumcision justify *access* [italics mine] to this procedure for families who choose it." "Access" is the euphemism employed by the AAP in its quest to ensure payment for circumcision by private insurers or government payers, especially Medicaid.

The report went on to review literature on nearly every affliction circumcision had ever been claimed to prevent or cure (diplomatically omitting masturbation, insanity, and rape), including penile and other cancers and an exhaustive list of sexually transmitted infections. None of these diseases is less common in the United States, where most males have been circumcised than in other developed countries, where circumcision is rare. But no matter. The Task Force members collectively created a masterpiece of smoky mirrors, contradiction, and equivocation, with a good dose of irrelevant discussion and outright nonsense thrown in.

Consider, to start, these contradictory statements in the AAP's 2012 Task Force Report:

"Benefits [of circumcision] outweigh the risks..."[19]

[versus]

"The true incidence of complications after newborn circumcision is unknown, in part due to differing definitions of 'complication' and differing standards for determining the timing of when a complication has occurred ..."[20]

[and]

"Based on the data reviewed, it is difficult, if not impossible, to adequately assess the total impact of complications because the data are scant and inconsistent regarding the severity of complications."[21]

As I read the report, I became increasingly incensed at its sheer duplicity. Purporting to review and honestly present the facts, AAP turned a blind eye to serious circumcision injuries and even deaths among American babies. In the section titled Major Complications, the Task Force admits to having excluded "severe and catastrophic injuries," including "glans or penile amputation, transmission of herpes simplex after mouth-to-penis contact by...Jewish ritual circumcisers...methicillin resistant Staphylococcus aureus infection, urethral cutaneous fistula, glans ischemia, and death, because they are so infrequent as to be reported as case reports."

Also glaringly absent from the 2012 report was any mention of the characteristics and functions of the male foreskin—the body part being recklessly hacked off by doctors 3,500 times every day, as though it were a dead branch during springtime garden clean-up. Unlike the extensive anatomical drawings offered in the Bioethics Committee's botched call for doctors to be able to nick little girls' genitals, the AAP Circumcision Task Force offered no drawing or diagram of the natural, intact penis. There was no description of the foreskin's double-layered structure with its own supply of nerves and blood vessels, no mention of the muscles that surround its opening, or its role in protecting the head of the penis from abrasion and the elements, or how it keeps bacteria from entering the urinary tract. Certainly nothing was said about the foreskin's role in allowing for a complete erection in adult men or about how it eases intercourse with its gliding and lubricating qualities.

And nobody mentioned the 19th-century justification for initiating male circumcision in Western English-speaking countries: to "cure" masturbation. Bringing up this information would have at least given readers a hint that the early physician promoters of medicalized circumcision knew all too well that the foreskin was a source of pleasure for both men and women. Rather, the opening paragraph of the report assures the reader that the surgical removal of some, or all, of the foreskin is "one of the most common procedures in the world"—failing to mention that only in the United States of America does this "procedure" masquerade as health care.

Indeed, the only mention of sex at all was the task force's statement that circumcision does not affect sexual satisfaction in men. The data for this assertion? Follow-up interviews with the Kenyan and Ugandan men who had been circumcised as part of the HIV campaign, and a rambling literature review including findings deemed not statistically significant or that were inapplicable to the U.S. context.[22]

Given that these men were questioned by the same group of researchers who had persuaded them to give up their foreskins, and that most of us are unlikely even to complain to our barbers about a bad haircut, the reliability of their responses seem suspect. More to the point, how could such data possibly be relevant to the experience of men who are cut as babies and who, by the time they reach sexual maturity, have lived for years with the consequent nerve damage and 24-hour a day chafing, abrasion, and desensitization of their penises? The authors, likely to have been cut themselves as babies, clearly misunderstand that a man with an incompletely healed circumcision wound and recently denuded glans might report "much greater penile sensitivity," but that this doesn't mean it feels good.

All policy statements from the American Academy of Pediatrics automatically expire five years after publication unless reaffirmed, revised, or retired at or before that time. The means that the AAP Task Force's Report (and Policy Statement) on Circumcision technically expired in 2017.

However, that has not stopped the popular press from repeating the pro-circumcision claims and recommendations contained in the 2012 document. Only in the Spring of 2023 did the web link for the 2012 Policy Statement add a note saying: *This policy automatically expired.*[23]

So long as the conclusions and recommendations remain intact and are not revised or rescinded by the AAP by public announcement and retraining of the Academy's members, the promulgation of this medically and ethically bankrupt report is likely to continue, to the tragic detriment of American-born boys.

Chapter Thirty-Five

LIVES LOST

On March 8, 2013, California-born Brayden Tyler Frazier died from organ failure caused by blood loss following his circumcision. He was eleven days old.

Posts on Facebook written by Brayden's Sacramento-area family members alerted the ever-vigilant intactivist community to the baby boy's struggle and ultimate passing. His grandfather posted that Brayden's circumcision wound wouldn't stop bleeding; it seems he had a clotting disorder. Some of the details—the exact date Brayden's foreskin was amputated, whether his parents and doctors knew about the bleeding problem before the circumcision, *who* cut off Brayden's foreskin—are unclear. What is clear is that Brayden would not have died if he had not had a circumcision. Posted on the Facebook account of Brayden's decline was a photo of his young father resting his arms on the bars of his very pale baby son's hospital crib, the letters **F A T E** tattooed on the fingers of his right hand.

Was it Brayden's fate to die from circumcision? I say no. If I believed it was his fate, why would I be doing this work? I believe—no, I *know*—that Brayden's death was due to what Leonard Glick, author of *Marked in Your Flesh*, has called a *profoundly evil act*: cutting the genitals of a tiny, innocent child. And every time I hear of a child, or an adolescent or adult, who dies as a result of having been genitally maimed as a child, I also know I can never stop working to end this serial maiming.

Unfortunately, those behind the serial maiming of babies and the adults they will become do not feel the same responsibility. A year before Brayden Frazier would bleed to death from his wound, Douglas Diekema, head of the Bioethics Committee that authored the FGM-lite proposal, had publicly denied the lethal nature of infant circumcision. He scorned, in particular, my colleague Dan Bollinger's published estimate that in the year 2010, 117 U.S. infant deaths were attributable to those babies' circumcisions.[24] Speaking in a 2012 interview on San Francisco Public Radio station KQED, Diekema flatly stated: *"There are not 117 deaths in the United States that are directly the result of circumcision."*[25]

Then, presumably in reference to baby Joshua Hoskins who died in 2010 from loss of blood following being circumcised while in the intensive care unit of a Kansas hospital, Diekema continued: "For example, there's at least one of these cases that gets trotted out that involved a very sick baby that was likely to die anyway, and his parents wanted him circumcised before his death. To attribute that to a circumcision is silly."[26]

I wonder if Dr. Diekema also would think it "silly" to attribute Brayden Frazier's death a year later to his circumcision? Was Brayden also "likely to die anyway" from his bleeding disorder, absent the circumcision and before any tests might have shown that his blood wasn't clotting properly? After all, Brayden's parents wanted him to be circumcised, or at least they signed a consent form to that effect.

And what about Jamaal Coleson, a toddler who died in 2011 after the surgical removal of his foreskin at one of New York City's most prestigious hospitals?[27] Nothing in the news reports about Jamaal's death suggests that the surgery was anything other than "routine" or "elective"—in other words, there was nothing wrong with this child or his penis. Jamaal's death was reported to be related to general anesthesia, presumably administered because local numbing agents (which according to news reports was the original plan) are inadequate for managing the agony and resistance of a two-year-old.

Jamaal's parents also would have needed to sign off on the surgery, showing that they, like Brayden's and Joshua's parents, "wanted him to be circumcised." If one accepts Dr. Diekema's premise that the circumcisions in all of these cases were the parents' legitimate choice, then it would be logical to hold the parents responsible for the deaths of their sons.

But I know well that not all parents—even those who sign a consent form—want their babies to be circumcised. Sometimes, it's just not part of their culture—for example, among non-Muslim, non-Jewish Europeans, Asians, and Latin Americans. Often, it's because parents intuitively know that this amputation is something no baby needs or should have to endure. But because the practice is so endemic in American medicine, it should come as no surprise that the system is designed to perpetuate it.

Thus, hospital administrators' claims that they accommodate the surgery as a "service" to their patients (note: no baby has ever requested this service, so who is the patient?), and doctors' and nurses' refusal to admit that they push it on mothers throughout pregnancy and delivery of their babies are nothing more than hollow denials of the coercion.

For years, my inbox and various circumcision-related social media sites have been replete with specific complaints about the pressure put on parents to sign a consent form and the hostility they face when they decline to allow a doctor to mutilate their sons. Intact America has been able to document and even quantify this pressure. In 2020, we commissioned a random-sample national survey on circumcision solicitation and found that expectant mothers are asked an average of *eight times* during their pregnancies and immediately post-partum if they want to circumcise their sons.

Pressure to circumcise is particularly fierce in U.S. hospitals, but one of the most poignant examples of physician solicitation I've heard about came from Ontario. Canada's infant circumcision rate is lower nationally than that of the United States, but the two countries share a common history of the practice, and in certain provinces it's common for private doctors to promote and carry out the surgery. Thus, in 2013, when Ryan Heydari was born in a Toronto area hospital, his Iranian immigrant parents were pressured by their family physician to circumcise him. Ryan's father initially said no. Local news quoted Mr. Heydari as saying, "Mother nature created us the way she intended us to be." But the pressure continued, and Ryan's foreskin was cut off when he was fourteen days old.

Eight days later, Ryan died from "hypovolemic shock," having lost forty percent of his blood since his surgery.[28] The email I received from Ryan's father, John Heydari, in response to a condolence letter I had mailed to the family nearly two years earlier, reveals not only the pressure, but also the marital conflict, around the circumcision decision and the ultimate death of this child.

Hello Dear Chapin thanks for your message lose my son Ryan caused me a lot of problems mentally and also me and my wife getting divorce because of my wife and family doctor force me to do the circumcision my son Ryan and it was terrible decision and I'm still suffering of depression

I try to Bring the doctors negligence up and sue them so far nothing's happened anyways thanks for following up and your message.[29]

You might notice that the deaths I mention here occurred several years before I undertook to write this book. It's not that babies have stopped dying from circumcision. It's not that doctors have gotten "better" at the surgery, or that the risks of it have somehow diminished.

Some intactivists spend time on Facebook, finding and reposting (often redacting the name of the original post's author) tragic stories of baby boys who are either struggling to survive after a circumcision-gone-south, recovering despite a crisis ("he's a champ; thank goodness he won't remember a thing"), or who have passed away ("It was God's will; he's with the angels now"). It disturbs me to see the way these posts are trolled by people whose opposition to circumcision results in attacks on parents whose babies became critically ill or died after being cut. These attacks spark defensiveness and even retrenchment, with some bereaved parents insisting—in another version of Dr. Doug Diekema's denial and in an echo of the technical causes of death on the death certificates—that the circumcision was not responsible for the child's death. Denial and delusion are self-serving responses but do nothing to protect the most vulnerable.

For all these reasons, at some point I stopped reading about babies' deaths from circumcision. It is simply too painful to contemplate. Instead of following such stories, I'm writing this book and hoping that you—the reader—will spread the word to others. Say NO if you are ever asked the question, "You're going to circumcise him, right?" And if anybody you know is expecting a baby boy, tell them, "Please, whatever you do, don't let the doctors cut his penis."

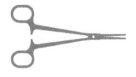

Chapter Thirty-Six

FAMILIES FALL APART

The newspaper reports saying that both of Ryan Heydari's parents were originally opposed to the circumcision and the contradictory email I received much later from Ryan's father (blaming his wife as well as the family's doctor) reflect something I have seen frequently in my own work. The pressure to circumcise placed on parents by authority figures such as doctors and nurses, or by members of their own family, can persuade even the most doubtful mother or father to waffle and to go along with the "experts," even if the other parent remains opposed. The consequences of the discord are amplified if the baby is cut, and tragic if something goes terribly wrong—something nobody can ever be prepared for.

One day, I got an email from a man named William (not his real name) who told me his wife was expecting in a couple of months, and the baby was a boy. He didn't want his son to be cut, but his wife was adamant. After a couple of short emails back and forth, we spoke twice over the phone. Our first conversation was factual. William, who had been cut as a baby, and his wife were both athletic instructors. They already had a two-year-old daughter. William was white and his wife was Black. He told me she thought foreskins were filthy, and that she had told him if he mentioned keeping their future son intact one more time, she would leave him.

Our second conversation was infused with William's anguish and despair. He wanted to know what options, if any, he had to stop the circumcision. I told him that even though a mother's signature on a "consent" form is usually all that's needed for the doctor to go ahead with the operation, if the other parent makes known to the doctor and the hospital staff, verbally *and* in writing, their fervent opposition, that parent might at least buy time and even get a court order staying the operation.

William feared that if he went all-out to protect his son's body, and his wife followed through with her threat to divorce him, he would lose his family life and be deprived of a close relationship with both of his children. He asked me, as he was asking himself, "Is this something I'm willing to end my marriage over?"

I'm not a psychologist or a marriage counselor. My view is, however, that if one partner in a couple is truly unbending over something so fundamentally important to the other partner, then the relationship is already foundering, if not lost.

My answer to William was, "Maybe. But only you can answer that."

I never heard from William again, so I don't know what happened with his son, or with his marriage. I fear the fact he didn't reach out again means that the baby was cut, and that he was either embarrassed to tell me, or believed I would think he lacked courage or had failed his son. I did send a couple of follow-up emails telling William my thoughts were with him and his family, which was (and still is) true.

In the years since I've been doing this work, I've seen many more instances where serious discord over whether to cut or not cut a son brings the relationship between the parents to the breaking point. Niki

S. is a young Pennsylvania mom, who appeared on a Philadelphia TV segment with me. When Niki's son was born, as her obstetrician laid the baby on her chest in the delivery room, he asked her about circumcision. She looked at her partner and he looked the other way.

The OB informed Niki that the doctor who would do the job would be by to see her the next morning. Sure enough, she was awakened a few hours later by a "really old" doctor with a clipboard in his hand, asking her to sign a consent form, which she did. She told me she knew as she did it that it was a mistake. This feeling was reinforced, first when her obviously traumatized son was returned to her and refused to nurse.[30] Later, when the doctor came to see her, he made a joke about his own shaky hands.

Niki told me her anguish over her son's circumcision tainted her previously harmonious relationship with the baby's father. In addition to resenting him for not backing her up when she showed uncertainty, she had started having horrible visions of her partner's own circumcision, his own mutilation, when they were having intimate relations. She told me, "Our relationship will never be pure again." Niki sought therapy and became a doula.

The Wicklunds are another family where discord over their son's circumcision nearly broke up the marriage, but ultimately resulted in reconciliation, activism, and healing. I met Elise and Tracy Wicklund in 2015, outside the Washington, D.C. convention center where the annual meeting of the American Academy of Pediatrics was being held. Twenty or so intactivist demonstrators were picketing with signs—many of them produced by Intact America. There on the sidewalk was a couple with a toddler daughter and a baby boy who looked to be around six months old lying on a padded blanket. Elise, the wife, was chatting with other demonstrators, while her husband Tracy quietly attended to the children. I joined the conversation between Elise and another young mother—a nurse—whose experience with her first son was similar to Elise's.

The Wicklunds live in Florida, and at the time baby Paxton was born, they disagreed about whether or not he should be circumcised. Elise was against; Tracy was pro-circumcision and adamant.

Despite Elise's opposition, at Tracy's insistence they made an appointment to have the baby circumcised in the pediatrician's office. As the appointment drew near, Elise's anxiety increased so they consulted with the pediatrician, who assured them that it would be quick (he actually said "just a snip"), that it wouldn't hurt, and that it was the right thing to do for their baby son.

The first time she changed Paxton's diaper after the surgery, Elise knew they had failed their son. Paxton developed a painful ulcer, adhesions and other complications that lasted a long time. He cried with every diaper change.

Tracy was quiet as he listened to his wife describe to me her deep depression, the rage she felt over having given in to the doctor's pressure, and her decision to speak out and start connecting with other mothers who had gone through the same experience.

After the event, we stayed in touch through the birth of two more children (the last one a boy who was kept whole), and an eventual reconstitution of the couple's relationship. Later, in a *Voices* post she wrote for Intact America, Elise described the importance of getting involved in the intactivist movement: "The darkness began to lift a little when I started connecting on Facebook with other moms going through the same thing. I joined a group of them at a protest in Washington, D.C..., and that's when I met Georganne Chapin from Intact America. Activism was empowering, and it drove my healing."

Tracy also has spoken out. In 2017, he wrote a letter for an Intact America fundraiser that has to be one of the bravest and most poignant confessions I have ever seen.

I'm a photographer, and the father of two daughters and a son. When my son Paxton was a month old, he was circumcised. I allowed it to happen. And since that day 18 months ago, my life has been a living hell.

I want to tell my story, in the hope that you will help Intact America, to make sure that no father will fail his son the way I failed Paxton.

When we found out that my wife Elise was pregnant with a boy, we talked about circumcision, and actually laughed at the dumb pro-circumcision arguments: "a boy should look like his father" or "he'll be made fun of in the locker room."

Elise didn't want to do it. But [like most American men my age, I'm circumcised]... I thought it was the normal thing to do. I made it [Elise's] burden to convince me otherwise. That's crazy. In every other thing in life, it's the opposite. You have to fight to convince somebody to DO something. But for circumcision, you have to fight to explain why you're NOT going to do it...

Elise was a wreck. But the doctor told us it was better for boys to be circumcised. I said I didn't want my baby to feel pain. He said it wouldn't hurt a bit. He even "cleared his schedule," so we could get it done sooner rather than later. His nurse told us how he played soft, soothing music during the surgery.

The first diaper change was when I realized the horror of what I'd allowed to happen to my baby son. I had actually believed the myth, "It's just a snip." Now, to see an open wound instead of his perfect, intact body. To hear his cries when we tried to clean and put Vaseline on him... I will never forget that. And I will never forgive myself.

I could shift the blame to that doctor. On some level, I knew he was lying—that his only concern was the $300 fee he'd collect—but I still agreed to it. I am responsible. Why did I go along, even though I knew it was wrong? I'm ashamed to say I went along because—although I was 40 years old—I didn't want to be the "weird guy on the block...."

I made it about me—not my son.

Everything has changed. My entire world is unraveling still. Elise can't do anything except speak out against circumcision. It's almost the only thing we talk about. And I try not to show how I feel, because if we both fall apart, then who will take care of the family?

As painful as it is for me to share how I failed my wife and son, I am grateful that Intact America is giving me this chance to tell my story. __

It's Father's Day soon. And I want to tell other men, other fathers, to stop defending, and start listening.

Tracy Wicklund

There's more. When their son Jaxon was born, Elise wrote: "There was no debate about circumcision. And we got no pushback from family—I think because for nearly three years I raged against it and told pretty much everybody I knew that circumcision was bullshit."

The Wicklunds have inspired me in ways I wouldn't have thought possible. Knowing the damage that circumcision has done, and having the good fortune to have not cut my own son, I have struggled over the years with judging other parents who didn't have the insight or fortitude to say NO. But because of my own upbringing—with parents who in many ways challenged the social status quo, protesting the war in Vietnam and defying racial segregation, but who nonetheless allowed my brother's genitals to be cut—I get how people can be inconsistent in ways that to others may seem hypocritical. And, of course, I have found it both useful and humbling to remind myself of examples in my own life where my actions have not always been consistent with my beliefs.

Parents, with infinitesimally few exceptions, love their children and want to do right by them. When faced with pressure from authority figures like doctors and other medical personnel, as well as older relatives or friends who have a vested interest (overt or unexplored) in pushing the circumcision status quo, it's no wonder how many give in and say yes. And even though my son was fortunate that I spared him from that surgery, I really did not know at the time the potential tragedy I was averting by saying no.

What so many people do not appreciate is that the damage to couples and families caused by circumcision of a son can surface many years later. Every intactivist is familiar with the name Jonathon Conte, a beloved intactivist who took his own life in 2016. Fewer Americans know the name Alex, a young British man who allowed a Canadian doctor to perform a circumcision on him, promising it would "cure" his tight foreskin. He lost all sensitivity in his penis and took his own life in 2017.[31]And early in 2023, a young Florida man whose name I am not at liberty to reveal left the world in despair and grief, caused not only by the physical effects of his circumcision but because his father refused to acknowledge that his suffering was legitimate, instead insisting that it had been the father's right to make that decision for his son.[32]

I can hear Douglas Diekema's words: "It's silly to attribute these young men's suicides to their circumcisions." Really? What could be more traumatic than the violent removal of a sexual body part, one that the violated individual witnesses every time he urinates, every time he gets an erection, every time he masturbates, every time he has sex or attempts to have sex? What is the impact of knowing that the person who was supposed to protect you did not? All of these are terribly difficult questions, ones that many of us would like to avoid. But to stop the cutting, we must confront them and take a position to stop the mutilation.

Chapter Thirty-Seven

WHAT'S SEX GOT TO DO WITH IT?

Everything. It's common sense, isn't it? Why would someone cut off part of a child's sex organs, if not to interfere with or somehow regulate their sexual impulses and behavior? How could cutting off a sexual body part *not* affect the mechanics and quality of the victim's sex life, sexual relationships, and psyche?

Before I go on, I must say that, despite years of armchair advocacy, only when my son thanked me for not allowing him to be cut did I begin to understand the profound consequences of that act.

Throughout human history and across cultures, the genital cutting of both males and females has been underlain by an obsession with regulating and controlling sexual activity and sexual pleasure. It's remarkable, then, that today—in 21st century United States of America—we double down and insist that removing the male prepuce (or foreskin), that part of the male anatomy associated over millennia with sexual potency and pleasure, has no impact on sexual potency and pleasure.

Here's a bit of trivia: What do Moses Maimonides (revered 12th century Jewish philosopher and physician) and John Harvey Kellogg (19th-20th-century American businessman, physician, and the inventor of breakfast cereal) have in common?

The answer: They both knew (or at least fervently hoped) that cutting off a man's foreskin would inhibit his sexual appetite, his own sexual pleasure, and the sexual pleasure of his sex partners. And that is precisely why each of them, eight centuries apart, promoted the surgery.

Maimonides was born in Cordova, Spain in 1135, around 3,000 years after Jews began circumcising. So, he didn't invent the practice. But here's how he explained circumcision and why he advocated for it.

...with regard to circumcision, one of the reasons for it is...the wish to bring about a decrease in sexual intercourse and a weakening of the organ in question, so that this activity be diminished and the organ be in as quiet a state as possible...The bodily pain caused to that member is the real purpose of circumcision. ...[V]iolent...lust that goes beyond what is needed [is] diminished. The fact that circumcision weakens the faculty of sexual excitement and sometimes perhaps diminishes the pleasure is indubitable. For if at birth this member has been made to bleed and has had its covering taken away from it, it must indubitably be weakened....[33]

Maimonides also observed women's preference for men with natural penises, citing this as further evidence that circumcision was necessary to keep everyone in line. "[Additionally,] it is hard for a woman with whom an uncircumcised man has had sexual intercourse to separate from him. In my opinion this is the strongest of the reasons for circumcision."[34]

Kellogg, born seven centuries later in Tyrone, Michigan, came from a family of Seventh Day Adventists. He was among an influential group of Victorian-era physician fanatics in America and England who believed that non-Jews should take up foreskin amputation to keep boys from engaging in the "dangerous and immoral practice of masturbation." He recommended that it be performed with no anesthetic, "as the pain attending the operation will have a salutary effect upon the mind, especially if connected with the idea of punishment."[35] Like Maimonides, then, Kellogg believed that the pain and cruelty of circumcision was its main point.

As the groundwork was being laid for widespread male genital cutting in English-speaking countries, Christian missionaries (many of them also commercial opportunists) from Britain and America were busy removing the penises from wood-carved male figures throughout the Western Pacific, including Australia, New Zealand, Samoa, and New Guinea. While studying anthropology as a Barnard undergraduate, I took a class in "primitive art," and was astonished to see that the penises of most male figures housed in museum collections and depicted in books had been lopped off or gouged out. Ostensibly, this practice made the art more acceptable in the eyes of the western world. I saw it as a manifestation of the missionaries' own immense sexual anxiety, and their efforts to justify their own cultural superiority by sexually humiliating so-called "uncivilized" peoples.

Since the 1960s, in large part due to the invention and availability of new contraceptive methods that gave women and couples more control over reproduction, Americans' attitudes toward sex and sexual pleasure have changed considerably. On television and in movies, sex is everywhere, whether romantic or transactional, and is portrayed ever more explicitly. We avidly follow the sex lives of celebrities, politicians, members of the clergy, gay people vs. straight people, and our neighbors. Women freely talk about their libido or lack thereof. They talk about their orgasms and how to satisfy themselves. Men talk among themselves and, since I have been leading Intact America, lots of them talk with me. I believe that this is because, as an older woman, I am regarded as safe.

It's no longer a taboo to talk about sex problems, and we are flooded with ads on TV and social media for drugs and other products created to remedy erectile dysfunction in men and vaginal dryness in women. It bears mentioning here that research has shown that circumcised men suffer from alexithymia (impaired ability to identify and describe one's emotions) at rates 20 percent higher than intact men, and are up to 4.5 times more likely to be diagnosed with erectile dysfunction than their intact peers.[36]

Unsurprisingly, then, sexual satisfaction and intimacy remain elusive, with women commonly complaining about their male partners' lack of emotional sensitivity and intimacy in bed, and incompatibility when it comes to the pace, aggressiveness, and duration of intercourse. (A common complaint I hear from women is that their partners "pound" them; this is a compensatory behavior resulting from the removal the foreskin with its many nerve receptors.) Men, of course, suffer immeasurably from problems they had no hand in creating and that hobble their ability to experience pleasure the way nature intended and, consequently, intimate relationships.

Remarkably, in an internet search on the topic, not one person in the dozen chat rooms I visited suggested that this pounding, pain, dryness, and other problems between American men and women might be caused, rather than by some inherent male emotional detachment or insensitivity to their partners, by a mechanical deficit. All because most American men are missing a vital part of their sex organ.

One reason we continue to deny the obvious is that—despite the popular obsession with our own and others' sex lives—our understanding of sex is rather vague, romantic, and primitive. Sex education in schools might delve into the mechanics of reproduction and pregnancy prevention and, as of late, it might address issues of consent. But our children, to their detriment, learn precious little about passion and lust and the human drive for emotional attachment, meaning they are unprepared for the power of these urges. Young people are intentionally kept ignorant about how male and female bodies are biologically primed, and the genitals (the male penis and the female vulva) exquisitely designed to enable and enhance sexual intercourse and make it pleasurable. Absent this information, it's not surprising that people are clueless about circumcision. **In fact, perpetuation of circumcision in American culture *depends upon* such ignorance.**

I've heard teenage girls say hateful things about boys who are not circumcised, and seen intelligent, educated professional women, including mothers of sons, grimace in disgust at the mention of an intact penis. If I could have a dollar (well, maybe ten dollars) to invest for every dumb foreskin joke or vulgar name for an intact man I've heard, Intact America could buy a thirty-second Super Bowl ad next time around. I've seen young doctors at professional conventions engulfed in giggles when they saw the Intact America banner listing Ten Reasons Not to Circumcise Baby Boys or a handout about functions of the foreskin.

On the other hand, countless men and women are beginning to pursue the truth. In August 2022, I recorded a segment on circumcision for a podcast called *Curiosity with Jon and Mike*.[37] The show's hosts are two guys from Texas. Jon is Latino and intact, and Mike is a white guy who was cut as a baby. Our rambling conversation lasted well beyond the hour that had been scheduled.

What Jon and Mike knew about circumcision was mostly limited to the popular explanations for the practice: "it's cleaner," "so a boy can look like his dad," "it prevents urinary tract infections," and "so your son won't be ridiculed" by his peers. The questions they posed, though, were mostly about the history of the practice—and about sex.

About halfway through the show, Mike asked me: "Does [circumcision] make sex less desirable? Are you going to want to have sex less?" And then he said, "I mean, shoot me straight. I'm circumcised. What am I missing out on here?"

"Well," I answered, "Wanting to have sex, that's your libido; that's your sexual desire. And only you know your libido." By not understanding libido, what the Victorians got wrong was thinking that cutting off the foreskin would stop boys from masturbating. It didn't.

I went on to answer Mike's last question. "Are you missing something? Yes. You're literally missing part of your penis, the foreskin."

"That's not a value statement," I added. "It's a simple fact."

Every conversation with a cut man about circumcision and sex ends up with this question being asked, either silently or out loud: *What am I missing?* Meaning: *What would sex be like for me if I had a foreskin?*

If you have been circumcised, you're missing blood vessels, muscle, specialized nerve endings, and other features unique to the foreskin and designed for the optimal performance, protection, pleasure, and satisfaction of the man—and his partner. Men with intact genitals experience sex the way nature intended.

The human body, down to every detail, is designed to work as a well-oiled machine. Every body part performs one or more particular function, and each of the body's systems (for example, the respiratory system, the cardiovascular system, the digestive system) is also exquisitely designed, with its respective components enhancing its owner's optimal wellbeing.

Unlike other body systems, though, the reproductive organs (including, of course, the genitals) work cooperatively with the reproductive system and genitals of persons of the opposite sex. That's how our species survives.

So, if we look at a penis with its prepuce intact, and discard the myths we've been told (e.g., the foreskin is "dirty," or it's "extra skin"), we see that it is an integral part of the penis. The nerves, muscle, and blood vessels of the foreskin are connected to the rest of the external male sex organs—the shaft of the penis, the frenulum, the scrotum, and the testicles. The foreskin functions throughout a male's life to protect the glans (head of the penis) from abrasion and other damage. Once the foreskin becomes retractable, its loose skin provides mobility and stretches to accommodate a full erection. Furthermore, the foreskin keeps the glans soft, pink, and moist. The glans of a circumcised man, on the other hand, develops a gray tinge, and becomes keratinized, toughened, over time due to abrasion and chafing.

Finally, an intact penis is a bit longer and a bit chubbier than a circumcised penis. In fact, if you were to remove the average double-layered male foreskin, open it up, and lay it flat, it would be nearly the size of a 3x5 index card. This means that a circumcised adult man has been robbed of 12 to 15 square inches of sensitive, mobile, protective tissue that God or nature meant him to have.

There's more. The ridged band on the male foreskin (removed during circumcision) contains thousands of Meissner's corpuscles, special light-touch nerve endings, located in glabrous (hairless) skin in other areas of the body, including the eyelids, lips, fingertips and palm of the hand.

During sex or masturbation, these nerve endings give a man feedback about where he is in the ejaculatory process. The frenulum ("little bridle"), the structure on the underside of the penis that keeps the foreskin in place (much as the frenulum under your tongue keeps it from flopping around inside your mouth) also contains Meissner's corpuscles.

This explains why in circumcised men, the frenal scar is often the most sensitive part of the penis, although some men have more or less of the remnant frenulum depending on the aggressiveness of the surgery. Also, circumcised men need more friction and longer strokes, usually for a longer period of time, to come to orgasm. Finally, because of the foreskin's mechanical design and lubricating function, the intact penis stimulates a woman and keeps the vagina from drying out during intercourse.

Thankfully, the genitals and the human body have many other points of pleasure. A woman I know can come to orgasm if someone spends a bit of time tenderly kissing her neck. But it is fair to say that the unwarranted removal of the male prepuce has marred the sex lives of tens of millions—no, hundreds of millions—of Americans.

I've become accustomed to hearing and answering questions like Mike's. It's disturbing to lay these facts bare. On the other hand, it can be profoundly liberating for a man to begin to comprehend that the reason certain things "never felt right" is, in fact, that they are not "right." And, furthermore, that they are not his fault. He was robbed and can only begin to comprehend what he is lacking by learning the facts that I am presenting here. This knowledge can go a long way toward instilling honest conversation and compassion into interpersonal relationships.

But for circumcision to stop, we have to be able to admit that over the past century, the majority of the male population in our country has been subjected to a needless surgery that has left them missing an important part of their bodies—often to devastating effect. I've spoken to many, many men like Mike—some of whom were vaguely aware that something was off, and others who lacked a clear idea of what had been taken from them until, after our conversation, they began to search for the truth.

I also get calls from older men who have known all their lives they were missing out. Some bleed every time they have an erection. Others experience pain from being cut "too tight" or they simply cannot perform sexually in a "normal" way (penile/vaginal intercourse) due to maiming. Their anger, grief, and frustration are palpable, and tragic.

One long-time intactivist told me recently that he knew from the time he was twelve years old that something was terribly wrong with his penis. In his mid-teens he embarked on a quest to read everything he could find about this practice of circumcision. The more he read, the angrier and more depressed he became. Finally, in the early 1980s he heard about Marilyn Milos's work and also read Edward Wallerstein's book, *Circumcision: An American Health Fallacy* (1980). His hopes for change were sparked. He spoke to a few men's groups to raise awareness, but quickly realized that the medical machine was too powerful, and that our movement was no match for the money that was being invested in keeping the public ignorant and keeping circumcision alive. At age 72, he told me with tears in his eyes that he's always wondered what his life might have been like if he'd been able to experience sex the way nature intended: "I will never know that pleasure."

I've spoken above of suicides directly linked to despair over circumcision—including one during the month I was writing the final chapters of this book. I know men whose lives have been blighted for years with night terrors, and who have been told by psychotherapists they've consulted that neither their sexual problems nor their inability to sleep peacefully through the night can possibly be related to having their genitals cut when they were little babies. How absurd is that?

As long as this wall of shame and silence pervades our society, another generation of boys is destined to grow up bearing the physical and psychological scars resulting from decisions made for them, often within hours of their birth. Those decisions —based on false narratives, pseudoscience and societal pressure—carry life-long consequences for the men they will become and everyone in those boys' and men's personal orbits.

Chapter Thirty-Eight

WHAT'S RELIGION GOT TO DO WITH IT?

Barely anything. Shortly after founding Intact America, with funds provided by our original donor, we hired a public relations and communications firm called M+R Strategic Services. With the support of Hudson Health Plan's Ted Herman, M+R took Intact America "public," with a professionally designed website, well-written and attractive materials, and a bold slogan: "Changing the way America thinks about circumcision."

The firm also helped us organize highly visible public-facing events. These included a kick-off press conference in New York City, and demonstrations during national conferences of the Centers for Disease Control (CDC), the American Academy of Pediatrics, and the American Congress of Obstetricians and Gynecologists. We also held a protest at a large hospital that was hosting an infant pain study comparing the respective pain responses of infants circumcised with two different circumcision devices—a nightmare scenario of exploiting real babies to conclude which of two instruments of torture hurt them the most. In addition, M+R landed me a handful of television appearances including a live interview with Tom Costello on the *Today* Show and one on MSNBC with Dr. Nancy Snyderman.

Bob Liff, M+R's press guy, traveled with us to some of these events. Approximately my age, Bob, who was Jewish, had worked in Jimmy Carter's administration and then as a political reporter for a prominent New York newspaper. He was one of a number of terrific consultants who, over the years, taught me things I had never realized I needed to know. Early on in our professional relationship, Bob told me he'd talked to his wife about an interesting new client, Intact America, and she asked him if he thought we were anti-Semites. "I told her 'no.'" he said.

That was the first time in the thirty years I had been speaking out against circumcision that I heard someone, albeit through a third person, question whether my position about child genital cutting arose from an antipathy toward Jewish people. But it wasn't the last.

A similar conversation took place with Allen Bromberger, an attorney well-known in social entrepreneurship circles who had helped craft the legal documents for the creation of Intact America. Allen—affable, super-intelligent and well-informed—is the person I still rely on for creative business advice and legal work. One day he arrived early to a board meeting. As we sat chatting, Allen mentioned that he'd gotten some raised eyebrows from colleagues and friends when he told them about Intact America. And in a recent conversation with his wife, she had asked him: "Are they anti-Semitic?"

Oh, interesting, I thought.

"What did you tell her?" I asked.

Like Bob Liff, Allen apparently had been surprised by his wife's question, and—after hesitating—had said, "No. No, they're not."

A third series of events also bears mentioning here. The board of directors of the two nonprofits I led at the time (Hudson Health Plan and the Hudson Center for Health Equity and Quality) had agreed to establish a shared services agreement with the newly formed Intact America project. The agreement gave us pro-rated office space and also allowed a couple of senior-level staff members from the health plan to work part-time on the Intact America project. One of these was Hudson's chief financial officer Howard Birnbaum. I would describe Howie's early reaction to the creation of IA as "curious to know more." He and his wife attended a large Reform synagogue in Riverdale, New York, and their two children had been raised in that tradition. When his firstborn, a son, became a father, Howie was given the honor of holding his grandson for the ceremonial ritual circumcision.

A short time later, Howie stopped at my open door, telling me he would be taking the afternoon off. "But I can't tell you where I'm going," he said. I was used to seeing the guys on the executive team clear out for Opening Day at Yankee Stadium, but it wasn't baseball season. So, I asked about the only other thing that came to mind.

"Are you going to a *bris*?" His embarrassed smile told me I'd guessed correctly. I said, "NO! I'm not letting you go! You can't take the afternoon off!" We both laughed as he left the office. Neither of us could have imagined that just a few years later, Howie would suggest to a young relative, pregnant with a boy and agonizing over whether to have him circumcised, that she reach out to me for information about the alternative. She chose the alternative (yes!) and is now a mom to two whole beautiful children, a daughter and a son.

As far back in my childhood as I can remember, religion played little part in my home life. I was christened in an Anglican church— deemed by my Greek relatives to be the closest thing in Honolulu to

Greek Orthodox ("high," but not Roman Catholic). When my mother left Hawaii for New Mexico, though, any prior religious affiliation was in her rear-view mirror. Hank, whom she met her first year in graduate school, claimed to be an atheist, and my mother began describing herself as agnostic. Generally speaking, religion was not part of the household discourse.

Our home was a gathering place for my parents' fellow graduate students. Among those who came to hang out and talk books, culture, and current events was a couple who talked about being Jewish. In my childhood ignorance, I assumed Jewish was just another denomination, like Presbyterian or Catholics. There was some conversation about the Holocaust, and I knew that six million Jews had been killed and also about the millions of Romani people (then referred to as gypsies) and other eastern Europeans. But World War II was as remote to fourth- and fifth- grade me as the American Revolution. I was certainly aware of racism, but I had no sense of what religious prejudice would look like.

Decades later, as I became involved in the intactivist movement, but prior to forming Intact America, I became friendly with a progressive Presbyterian minister in New York's Hudson Valley where I still live. The father of two circumcised sons, Reverend Christian Iosso was not only willing to open his mind about a subject he'd given little thought to over the years, but after our conversations he surprised his rather staid congregation by delivering a Sunday sermon against the genital cutting of children—all children.

I understand the important role religion plays in many people's lives. I also appreciate any religion or denomination that advocates for the protection of the most vulnerable among us. With regard to child genital cutting, though, I believe unequivocally that the only legitimate role religion can play is to condemn that practice based on humanitarianism, morality, respect for individual autonomy, and compassion for the child whose wellbeing will be compromised ever after.

Somewhere around 1.4 million baby boys lose their foreskins to circumcision surgery each year in the United States. Only 4.2 million people (1.7 percent of the U.S. population) identify as Jewish by religion, with an additional 1.5 million (0.6 percent) identifying as Jewish but of no religion.[38]

Even if the birth rate among Jews was the same as the birth rate in the general population (it is lower), and if every baby boy born to Jewish parents underwent a ritual *brit milah* (many Jews do not; they opt for hospital circumcision, or forgo circumcising their sons altogether), the maximum number of circumcisions undertaken in the United States as Jewish rituals in a given year would be 24,000 out of 1.4 million. (Muslims, who make up only 1.7 percent of the U.S. population, also commonly see to it that their sons are circumcised, with no attendant religious ritual.)

In light of these facts, it is utterly illogical to link opposition to circumcision with religious discrimination. Rather, circumcision in the United States is a textbook example of the runaway fee-for-service medical industry, creating pathologies, building careers, and making money from excessive and high-cost screenings, drugs, and interventions of little value to people. "Routine" male circumcision, the most common pediatric surgery and one that treats no illness and has no therapeutic purpose, is a stunning example of this blatant money grab.

Over the years, my conviction has only grown that—except for stoking the fear that siding with the rights of the child might brand one as an anti-Semite—the American circumcision industry has nothing to do with religion. Unfortunately, doctors and hospitals and others who benefit from the penis business exploit this myth in order to defend the status quo and to profit from an indefensible human rights violation perpetrated on baby boys.

Chapter Thirty-Nine

HOW BIG IS THE PENIS BUSINESS?

Huge. One of the first questions people ask me when I tell them about the penis business is: "How much does a circumcision cost?" The answer is: "It depends on whether you're asking what a doctor or hospital charges, or how much money the practice of circumcision generates (and thus costs the payers) overall in the American medical industry."

Answering the question about charges is difficult because they vary from doctor to doctor, patient to patient (depending on their insurance or lack thereof), hospital to hospital, by geographical location (not only state to state but whether urban or rural), and whether the payer is Medicaid or another governmental program, the parents' employer, a commercial insurance company, or the parents themselves. In cases where the mother and baby are uninsured or (at the other end of the economic spectrum) if parents want someone fancier than who their insurance will cover, then doctors bill retail—and the fee is determined by what the market will bear. The only thing "routine" about newborn circumcision in terms of cost is that it is always a rip-off.

A prestigious obstetrician or urologist practicing in a fancy hospital in an affluent city can demand upwards of $2,500 to pry away, clamp and cut off your baby's foreskin. If you're a middle-class parent in a middle-class town, you'll probably find someone willing to do the same thing for $500 or less. In addition, hospitals add fees for the procedure room, nursing staff, supplies, and equipment (including single-use circumcision kits, gauze, and petroleum jelly for bandaging the baby's fresh circumcision wound). These fees vary widely and are either hidden in a global bill or listed separately, the latter leaving a parent to wonder how on earth a travel size tube of petroleum jelly and a small packet of gauze can cost more than a dinner out). I recently saw an online complaint from a mom who had been billed $600 by the doctor, $20 for "pharmacy," $91 for supplies and an additional fee of $2,200 by the hospital for her son's circumcision.[39]

But doctor and hospital charges are only the beginning. My colleague and Intact America board member Dan Bollinger has calculated the total cost of infant circumcision in the United States, including doctors' fees, facility bills, and the longer length-of-stay in the hospital for mother and baby because of scheduling issues. In addition, Dan estimates the cost of circumcision repairs (around 2.8 percent of cut boys require such surgery, referred to in the trade as "revisions"), some done for aesthetic reasons ("not enough skin taken off"), and some that attempt to correct serious medical errors. He also counted other expenses incurred by cut men and their partners over a lifetime, including erectile dysfunction drugs (circumcised men are 4.5 times more likely to be diagnosed with ED),[40] and even personal lubricants (a circumcised penis is drier than an intact penis). Considering that approximately 1.4 million baby boys are victims of foreskin amputation every year in the United States, Bollinger estimated that the total money spent in 2020 as a direct result of "routine" infant circumcision was $5,685,000,000—nearly six billion dollars.[41]

Even that figure is not where the penis business ends.

Shrouded in mystery is the foreskins-for-sale racket, wherein freshly severed foreskins are sold to the cosmetic and bioengineering industries so that their fibroblast cells can be processed and used in fountain-of-youth skin creams or artificial skin for burn victims. In 2013, television personality Oprah Winfrey began advertising the virtues of SkinMedica, an anti-wrinkle face cream made from human foreskin fibroblasts that promised to "rapidly restore the skin's barrier and moisture balance."

SkinMedica claimed that it hasn't bought a foreskin in twenty years—that just one "donated" foreskin is the gift that keeps on giving.[42]

Except that it wasn't a gift. Even if the original foreskin was purchased, it wasn't purchased from its rightful owner, but rather almost certainly from the hospital where the baby was circumcised. Oprah was picketed in several cities where she appeared following the scandal, but eventually the story died down. Or died down sufficiently, so that five years later, Sandra Bullock, with no visible shame, appeared on the Ellen DeGeneres show to trot out her new youthful look and talk about the micro-needling procedure that "pushes a substance" under the facial skin.

"What is that substance?" Ellen interrupted to ask.

"It is an extraction from a piece of skin ... from a young person far, far away," Sandra answered.[43]

"It's foreskin from a Korean baby!" Ellen blurted out.

As a matter of fact, when it comes to the private industry trafficking in babies' foreskins, complexity, chaos, and confusion are intentional creations of a system that benefits financially by keeping consumers (and even policymakers) in the dark.

Over the years, I've asked many nurses, physicians and hospital administrators what happens to babies' foreskins after circumcision. "They go into the trash," is the answer I'd grown accustomed to hearing.

But one day a couple of years ago, I was speaking to a private practice nurse-midwife who, along with her partners, delivers babies at a large teaching hospital. None of the midwives in her practice do circumcisions. She told me it's mostly the obstetricians or medical residents who do the surgery at her hospital.

So, I asked the question, "What happens to babies' foreskins after circumcision?"

She didn't need to think before answering, "They go straight to the pathology lab."

"What do they do with the foreskins in pathology? Where do they go from there?" I asked her.

She said she wasn't sure, but she'd be ask around and let me know the answers to my questions. When she hadn't returned my calls after a couple of weeks, I sent her an email reminding her of our conversation and asked if she'd be an informal advisor to Intact America. She wrote back and said she supported "the cause," but wouldn't be able to help us. Similar conversations with nurses who worked in large hospitals affiliated with academic medical centers told me that staff in these facilities are discouraged, if not prohibited, from revealing the practices around the disposition of human tissue, and about any relationships (presumably contractual) that exist between the human tissue industry and these medical centers.

What we do know, though, is that you can do an online search for "human foreskin fibroblasts" and several companies and websites offering this material for purchase will pop up. One company called Lifeline Cell Technology offers "Human Dermal Fibroblasts – Neonatal, Primary" for $554.60 plus a $78 delivery charge. The site describes the product as "isolated from neonatal human foreskin [from many donors] and cryopreserved after primary culture to ensure the highest viability and plating efficiency."[44] Even Amazon offers "Human Neonatal Foreskin" for $407.15. (I didn't complete the order; the listing has a one-star review.)[45]

A 2021 article in *Discover* magazine describes the current status and future potential for using human foreskin fibroblasts to fight such afflictions as cancer, Parkinson's disease, and Alzheimer's.[46] The article begins with the obligatory assurance that "Circumcision ranks among the world's most common surgeries (and one of the oldest)," and then remarks: "After its removal, most foreskin is tossed as biological waste—but when they're kept around, the leftover cells have proven a vital asset to medical research."

In an upbeat reference to "[the] cells' next adventure," the author lists the many future applications of the miraculous infant foreskin for regenerative medicine, repeating a trope I've seen before: that the fibroblasts from just one baby's foreskin "can be multiplied to cover several football fields." She also mentions that "a number of beauty products include baby foreskin." Finally, she assures the reader that, "While working with newborns' cells may sound eery [sic], scientists must follow strict consent guidelines to obtain them."

The *Discover* article gives no figures, but a simple Google search reveals that the human tissue industry is expected to reach $31 billion in sales by the year 2030. Keep in mind that this does not include the untold government, foundation, and corporate support for university buildings, research centers, and academic salaries in medicine and the fields of biotechnology and bioengineering. Also, remember that academic medical centers and universities, as "nonprofit entities," pay no taxes, though they reap massive revenues from private industry. This tax avoidance adds to the astronomical earnings produced from the penis business.

For those who benefit financially from foreskin removal, whether for commerce or simply as a fee-for-service medical procedure, it's imperative to maintain the economic pipeline(s) that will fill entrepreneurs' pockets. Thus, the prenatal, labor, birth and immediate post-partum experience of women who give birth in American hospitals is punctuated with the type of high-pressure sales tactics that we normally associate with scams.

But no matter how much or how little money this enterprise generates, the removal of the foreskin from its rightful owner—the child—violates the most basic bioethical principles of informed consent and patient autonomy. When foreskins are trotted down the big, shiny hospital corridor to a lab that will test them for viruses or pathogens, and then turn them over to a representative from a bioengineering company, no matter what form a parent might have signed, this activity constitutes outright tissue trafficking.

From an ethical standpoint, when it comes to minors, the language associated with using one person's body parts for another's benefit is pure euphemism. The term "donor" implies a voluntary, altruistic act on the part of the person whose tissue is relinquished, and the assumption that the potential recipient is worthy of the "donation."[47] These fallacious assumptions underlies the excuse I've heard often: "Well, the foreskin is useless to a baby; this way, thank goodness, it can help an unfortunate burn victim."

Of course, we know that no baby can be a donor. No baby *volunteers* to have his foreskin severed. The worthiness of the purpose or the recipient for which the stolen tissue is used is irrelevant.

What permits us to disregard basic ethical principles regarding people's rights to their own bodies is the ridiculous but much promulgated myth that the foreskin in its natural state on the body of a baby or man is worthless, inconvenient, dirty, or even dangerous. It's the ultimate twist of irony that parents will *pay* to have this body part removed from their child, and then allow anonymous strangers (persons or corporations) to profit from that body part.

First, the doctor who cuts off the foreskin is paid, then the hospital sells the foreskin, then the company breaks down the foreskin into its component parts and sell that material. Finally, the owners or shareholders of the company profit... And voilà! A useless piece of ugly, dirty flesh has become a life-saving medical treatment for a nameless and faceless accident victim, or a beauty concoction for a wealthy woman or man to rub into their face and neck.

We don't know exactly how freshly severed foreskins are trafficked from hospitals to the companies that process them and resell their biological components. We don't know exactly how or where the components are, in turn, transformed into commercial products. Neither do we know how much money is made as a result of the commercial sale of babies' foreskins. It doesn't help that the line between pure biomedical research and commercial ventures relying on human tissue is often blurry and that economic partnerships between industry and universities are secretive. Hopefully, one day a hard-nosed investigative journalist will take up this cause, expose those who reap the profits, and challenge the legitimacy of this massive, hidden sector of the penis business.

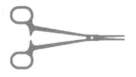

Chapter Forty

CIRCUMCISION CUTS THROUGH US ALL

Ever since I attended my first intactivist gathering in Washington, D.C. in 2003, I have been struck and intrigued by the socio-economic, educational, religious, and political diversity of the people in the movement. Now, two decades later, and fifteen years after becoming the founding director of Intact America, I can say that intactivism has grown exponentially—and that this diversity remains one of its most remarkable features.

Dean Pisani, the Texas businessman whose financial generosity made possible the founding of Intact America, mentioned exactly this when talking with a reporter about our first gathering in Dallas, where Intact America was born: "Here I was, sitting at the table with a bunch of people I'd never even drink a beer with, talking about genitals."

I knew exactly what Dean meant. Over the years, I have met, corresponded with, and developed close relationships with people whose backgrounds and positions on various contentious issues (abortion, guns, and vaccines, for example) bear little resemblance to my own. Conversely, I have moved away from people I had long considered to be peers, because they either dismissed my information or belittled the validity of my activism, often while arguing that cutting boys' genitals is for their own good, and "nothing like what *they* do to girls." Thankfully, for me personally and for intactivism overall, the friends I've lost are far smaller in number than the friends who've stuck with me and the many wonderful new friends and colleagues I've met through this work.

There's a very good reason for the intactivist movement's diversity: the violation that is infant circumcision literally cuts across every sector of our society. While the practice took hold in medicine during the early part of the 20th century, it was not until after World War II that forced foreskin removal became virtually universal for baby boys born in the United States. This means that around 80 percent (maybe more) of American men over the age of eighteen, and a marginally lower percentage of younger males in this country, are living with penises that have been surgically reduced in size and compromised in sensitivity and function.[48] It means that most women who grew up in the United States have never seen an adult man's intact penis, or even a baby's (except, perhaps, for a glance at their newborn sons' natural body before the "routine" surgery that would maim him).

The ubiquity of circumcision means that despite differences in age, income, race, ethnicity, educational level, religious beliefs or lack thereof, political affiliation, sexual orientation, or urban versus rural roots, the vast majority of Americans living today share a horrifying, though largely unacknowledged, commonality. For men, this means a violent assault on their genitals during their infancy or very early childhood, and lifelong deprivation of a full sexual experience. For women who have sex with men, this means the perpetual presence of a ghost in the bedroom, interfering with both pleasure and intimacy. Additionally, most parents of any sex or gender share the commonality of having been pressured to betray their male children by allowing a stranger, or someone they barely know, to cut these boys' genitals, and most have given in to the pressure. And, of course, the individual actors who actively participate in the circumcision industry—doctors and nurses, in particular—are themselves victims of the same practice they inflict on others.

A shared experience is not necessarily a recipe for solidarity, especially if that experience involves trauma or victimization and especially if the victims are men. I believe that's why there's still so much resistance to talking about circumcision in today's America and why it's so critical to see hostility toward our message as an understandable response by people whose stories have yet to emerge, even within their own psyches. Every day, we face the challenge of engaging and rousing those who have been silent, encouraging them to speak out. It's particularly difficult to do this across the lines that divide us in other ways. This is why we must continually work to frame our messages with respect, sensitivity, and empathy toward our audiences, as well as those we have yet to recruit.

Race is one of those dividing lines. I've spoken a lot about this problem with my friend Shelton Walden, who for many years hosted a radio program on New York City's Pacifica radio station WBAI, where he interviewed guests about many topics, including circumcision. When I asked Shelton recently to sum up why he thinks Black people are underrepresented in the intactivist movement, he answered succinctly: "There's a perverse disregard for and dismissal *by Black people* of Black men and their physical and mental pain." Shelton continued, "I've been told many times that circumcision is a *white* issue, not important to Black people, and that I have no business discussing it publicly."

Another Black intactivist, Tora Spigner, works as a nurse in the labor and delivery unit of a hospital in Berkeley, California. She told me that, in her experience, circumcision is a point of conflict within the Black community—that people are either adamantly opposed to it or adamantly in favor of it—there's no "in-between."

Other people I've spoken with say they believe the hygiene argument used to push circumcision has particular power when directed to Black Americans, who have been stigmatized through the country's history as unclean.

The explicitly racist history of circumcision in the United States began in the late 19th century with calls by a prominent physician named Peter Remondino. In addition to claiming that circumcision could cure or prevent scores of diseases or conditions, and that males born with short foreskins were more intelligent than those born with normal or long foreskins,[49] in 1901, Remondino had begun to call for "the wholesale circumcision of the Negro race." Dr. Remondino, who had been a surgeon in the Union Army during the Civil War, described Black men's foreskins as combining "the extra vitality and proliferation of the preputial tissue with the strong animal vitality of the negro." He proposed foreskin removal as "an efficient remedy in preventing the predisposition to discriminate raping so inherent in that race."[50]

If disseminated with sensitivity by reputable spokespersons in the Black community, including current chroniclers of racism in American medicine (for example, Harriet Washington, Isabel Wilkerson, and medical historian Dorothy Roberts), this information will, hopefully, spark greater community activism against this form of medical abuse. If conveyed in a sensitive way by the proper messengers, this kind of information can go a long way to activating people who might otherwise erroneously claim—as did Shelton Walden's detractors—that circumcision is a "white" issue.

This also applies to educating other minority groups in the United States who come from countries with no history of routine child circumcision. Latina mothers face disproportionate pressure to circumcise, with the intimation that this will make their sons fit in better with their peers. We know from numerous anecdotes that many immigrants from Central and South American countries do not understand the word circumcision or what the surgery entails. Indeed, I have been told by various Latina women that they believed that retracting their son's foreskin, as they had been taught by other female relatives or even their pediatricians, was actually a "circumcision."

Education can not only forewarn and forearm such women, but also can enlist them in peer group activities and community activism. While pressure to circumcise occurs across all socioeconomic levels in the Black and Latinx population, calls by the American Academy of Pediatrics to improve "access" to circumcision in the form of Medicaid payments for low-income and minority babies only further reveals the racism in such solicitation. Another key element of community education, then, is the information that Medicaid has made the procedure "free" in most states as a trick to get women to agree to the "benefit," and they should not hesitate to say no to this unnecessary surgery for their sons.

In striving to protect all children, we must work harder to identify and address misinformation, misunderstandings, and unspoken conflicts regarding race, class, and culture. Cultivating, recruiting, and supporting trusted spokespersons from within the various ethnic communities is imperative. Everyone has a circumcision story or will at some time in their American life. Circumcision cuts through us all.

Chapter Forty-One

SKIN IN THE GAME

Perpetuating the myth that circumcision is beneficial, if not necessary, to the health and well-being of the U.S. population has required the participation, willing and unwilling, of a huge cast of characters. Now, a century-and-a-half after the custom began as a medical practice, virtually every American alive has "skin in the game" of circumcision.

"Skin in the game" is a phrase that has been used in business since the 1980s and has been attributed to Warren Buffett. Since then, the phrase also has been used in popular culture as signifying that one has incurred risk (monetary or otherwise) by participating in an enterprise or actions in a particular business, sport, social, or artistic arena. As used by Intact America, "skin in the game" is an intentional play on the word "foreskin," the essential body part that is needlessly removed by medical doctors from nearly three-quarters of all baby boys born in the United States, and implies that we are all inextricably linked through our participation in that enterprise.

- For parents, it means that they fought off, or paid money, to someone wishing to cut off part of their children's bodies. If the latter, when the awareness sets in, they have to cope with remorse, regret, and—all too often—the pain and resentment of their sons.

- For cut men, it means that someone made money so they could lose a part of their body and that they are suffering the physical, sexual, and psychological consequences of the amputation.
- For doctors (many who themselves are also victims), it means having been taught to repeat the trauma by cutting other victims and participating in the commerce of the penis business.
- For spouses, partners, and lovers of cut men, it means coping (often unconsciously) with the physical and psychological consequences of having a partner who was sexually assaulted when he was an infant or small child.
- For our society, it means that most males have grown up with a baseline experience of sexual assault and its ongoing trauma, which then is (subconsciously or consciously) perpetrated across future generations.

Accomplice, facilitator, witness, victim, and perpetrator—all have skin in a tragic, money-driven game that thrives on surgically assaulting days-old male babies and that has produced profoundly harmful consequences in American culture over the past 150 years.

Fifteen years ago, when my friend Lucie Saunders asked me how I got into "this penis business," I thought the answers were simple—and obvious.

Isn't it a travesty that half of all new babies in the United States are born with a price tag on their normal, healthy genitals?

Isn't it obvious that removing unique, functional tissue replete with nerves, muscle, and blood vessels will make a boy's penis smaller and less sensitive for the rest of his life?

Isn't it pure hypocrisy to condemn forced genital surgery on girls as "mutilation" and "sexual assault," while defending forced genital surgery on boys as harmless and "for their own good?"

If these rhetorical questions made people uncomfortable, I figured they simply hadn't thought or read or heard enough about the issue. And that they would come around when they learned the truth. Obviously, I had underestimated the power of the forces (including personal and institutional self-interest) undermining the common-sense position that babies and children should be protected from unnecessary genital surgery.

The resistance and defensiveness I was witnessing reflected the near stranglehold the custom of unconsented-to male genital cutting has on the people of this country.

- Parents who have signed off on circumcising their sons, who later realize as teenagers or adults that they are missing something, do not want to feel guilty or bad about themselves. "We didn't know," they would say when their sons asked why; or they'd respond, "That's in the past. Get over it." They had no desire to listen to me or anyone else who might make them feel bad about their ignorance or negligence—or even to acknowledge remorse and regret.

- Nurses who were taught to follow orders and not challenge authority facilitate baby cutting to keep their jobs. Doctors who have been trained to deny the harm they inflict on hapless infants. Most tragically, the massive denial and dissociation of this act leaves no impediment to repeating the trauma day after day, year after year.

- Many boys and men who, when they realize they have been cut, have been too devastated and too ashamed to publicly acknowledge that they lost a part of their body behind closed doors to a system that made money from that act.

- Those who have not yet learned the details of the assault live with subconscious memories of the damage inflicted on their vulnerable baby bodies, damage that persists to this day. Ironically, like their assailants, they have a vested interest in continuing to repress their pain and rage, no matter the physical or psychological harm to themselves.

- Most girlfriends and wives have never seen an intact penis, and do not realize that their significant other is missing the most sexually sensitive part of his penis. Others know intuitively that something is off but don't ask questions, fearful of what they don't know or understand.

- Male spouses, lovers, and partners are also likely circumcised and accept a partner's circumcised penis without question.

- Ten out of ten babies say NO to circumcision, but their cries are ignored.

The resistance to our message by those with skin in the game was not surprising. But what shocked me was the desperation of the mainstream media, while purporting to be objective, to defend the scam.

An interview on MSNBC shortly after we launched Intact America in 2009 serves to illustrate the desperation of the medical profession and the mainstream press in their quest to defend circumcision.[51] On "Dr. Nancy," host Nancy Snyderman (a surgeon and medical reporter) began by revealing that her son was circumcised, and that she'd made that decision "for a lot of personal and medical reasons." She then launched into a rambling and conclusory monologue, ending with: "If we know that viruses and bacteria live under foreskin, and that hygiene can be a problem for any boy, I don't care what culture, and we know that HIV transmission rates are significant, how can you not draw a parallel between Africa and the United States when we're just talking about infection transmission?"

Easy, Dr. Snyderman! "We teach our children how to brush their teeth, how to clean their ears, and we certainly teach our girls how to wash their genitals," I responded. "There's no reason we can't teach our boys the same thing."

I also pointed out that the researchers in the African studies she referred to were most emphatic that condoms must still be used to prevent sexual transmission of disease, because HIV is spread through blood and semen. I didn't say this, though I wished later I had: No study, ever, has implicated unwashed penises as a factor in the transmission of HIV.

Also invited to the interview was pediatrician Laura Jana. Dr. Jana nodded approvingly as Dr. Nancy told the world that her son was circumcised (because "hygiene can be a problem for any boy..."). Jana then argued that the "African studies" have provided "potentially medically relevant data that might make it more important to give parents information about *the reason to circumcise*" (my italics). Before I could state the obvious—that with that kind of equivocation, you can make a case for just about anything—Jana went on to cite her expertise as an author who wrote a book about babies and whose mother was head of a national AIDS commission.

Both the host and her guest interrupted me as I pointed out that no plausible biological mechanism for the supposed reduction in HIV transmission among circumcised males had been identified, and that the focus on male circumcision meant that *women* faced a higher risk of getting AIDS. Incidentally, as we knew they would, the "African studies" have fallen flat in terms of preventing HIV transmission.[52] Rather, they have resulted in the mutilation of millions of Black African boys and men[53] and a massive international business in one-time-use, potentially contaminated circumcision kits, which then get tossed into the landfills. All of this is occurring at the same time the international health community strives to end the genital cutting of girls.

On Fox News in 2011, Megyn Kelly invited me to her show "for a fair and balanced debate" the day after I testified in front of the Massachusetts legislature in support of a circumcision ban for minors in that state (it didn't pass).[54] Megyn's other guest, Dr. Marc Siegel, was a physician and Fox network commentator. Dr. Siegel refuted my claim that circumcising a baby is a risky and unethical undertaking by countering that removing a baby's foreskin was no different than deciding to cut his umbilical cord. (Yes, he really said that.)

On display here, of course, was both arrogance and shameless ignorance on the part of the defenders of circumcision. They, too, had skin in the game and desperately needed to defend their investment. The network, of course, also was an investor, and therefore lacked objectivity and common sense. No self-respecting journalistic enterprise would do a segment on modern-day sex slavery and invite a sex trafficker as a so-called expert to present "the positive side" of that phenomenon.

The biggest challenge Intact America faced when we were formed—despite decades of actions taken to protest baby genital cutting—was the effective silencing of voices wishing to speak the truth about circumcision.

To be successful, we needed to find every single opportunity to make our position and our stories heard.

One such opportunity occurred shortly after the American Academy of Pediatrics report on circumcision was released in 2012, It illustrated how the public and political inevitably overlap with the personal when it comes to circumcision, extending to the private and family lives of the experts promoting the practice In November 2013, another intactivist group based in the New York area organized a weekend protest in front of the house of Dr. Susan Blank, pediatric HIV specialist who had headed the American Academy of Pediatrics Task Force that issued the 2012 smoke and mirrors report.[55] The group, led by Anthony Losquadro, carried signs calling out Dr. Blank for her irresponsible embrace of neonatal circumcision among American babies as potentially useful in controlling HIV transmission.

I remember thinking, "Well, that's novel"—not the protest itself, but the decision to take it to a relatively quiet residential street in one of New York's outer boroughs on a weekend when the doctor was likely to be home. The demonstrators clearly had calculated that if they picketed the New York City Department of Health during business hours, when the streets were full of people and Dr. Blank's office was many floors above ground level, the protest would be unlikely to reach its intended target. The sidewalk in front of her home, on the other hand...that was clever. Imagine my surprise, though, when I received a call from a former colleague, whom I'll call Peggy, who held a high-level position at the Department of Health.

Soon after starting Intact America, I'd told Peggy, a neighbor at the time, about my new organization. She had seemed interested, but the conversation was brief. Now, Peggy began the call with small talk, and then asked me about Intact America's activities. It turned out she believed we were behind the protest at Dr. Blank's home. I said we were not, but I knew some of the people in the group, and we shared common goals. She then asked if I could "call off" the protesters. It seemed that Dr. Blank was particularly offended that her adolescent son had to witness people protesting circumcision in front of the family home.

Now, while I couldn't claim credit for the protest, I wasn't about to condemn it, either. "Seems to me," I said, "that a 12-year-old boy certainly knows he's circumcised and might even know that his mother just authored a report promoting the practice. Perhaps Dr. Blank needs to talk with her son."

The second thing that set me back on my heels after becoming involved in the intactivist movement was the immense, debilitating grief and its related emotion—anger—among circumcision survivors and the people in their social and family constellations.

As my voice became more prominent, I began to receive letters, emails and phone calls in growing numbers. Some of these were from cut men themselves, some from parents of angry and rejecting sons, and some from partners trying to cope with physical or psychological problems resulting from the wounds that had been inflicted on one (or both) of them as a child.

Every day, I asked myself, *How could I not have anticipated this?* And then, *What could I have done to better prepare myself?*

I should have been asking the same questions about my personal life, it turns out.

I'd known for a long time that many shoes were yet to drop. I suppose that's always true, in that life is full of both beginnings and endings, but I can see now how taking on Intact America helped me to find new meaning in my life as other sad events, many of them inevitable, began to occur.

In 2009, just months after agreeing to lead the start-up as unpaid executive director (I already had a salary from Hudson Health Plan and felt it was important to use donor funds for other purposes), my personal life took several dramatic turns. First, my son Ernesto came back from the West Coast with a college degree, two dogs, and a slew of health problems. His return home helped to catalyze the end of my nine-year relationship with D. I had felt for a long time that we had no future as a couple, largely because of our difference in age. I didn't want to drag a much younger man into my own senior years, so when D announced that he needed to move out, I didn't protest. But I took no time to process that loss, and certainly did not—until years later—fully acknowledge the pain the break-up caused for both of us.

Second, the progressive dementia that had seized my always vibrant and driven mother and robbed her of her mind finally took her life in 2012. Over time, I had been adjusting to the reality that she would never return to being able to participate as an advisor and sounding board for my life and work. When she finally passed over to the other side, though, instead of taking the time to feel her absence, I focused instead on my relief that that she had been freed from her body and her mental prison, and buried myself in my work.

The third was, beginning in 2012, the somewhat protracted end of Hudson Health Plan. It started with a proposal from a much larger insurer to acquire the company I had created and shepherded nearly from its inception. Members of my board of directors had been getting rest-less, anxious to monetize the non-profit, something many of them had mentioned repeatedly over the years. I understood the business forces at work in our industry, but because of the turmoil in my personal life, as well as my excitement about Intact America, when executing the Hudson Health Plan transaction, I neglected to think adequately about my own future, and thus made errors I regret to this day.

Shockingly, as this transaction was unfolding and less than two years after my mother's passing, my brother Chip died. He had been living with chronic mental and physical illnesses since the mid-1980s, and we had all become accustomed, as had he, to his surviving ups, downs, and various crises. And despite the challenges he faced, includ-ing recent bouts of paranoia and confusion due to the breakdown of his vital organs, my own relationship with Chip remained a source of warmth and stimulating conversation for both of us. I especially loved talking with my brother about music and to this day marvel at the hundreds of CDs he left organized (mostly) in boxes, ranging from old-time rock & roll to Americana to Louisiana blues to Pink Floyd and Eric Clapton to Judy Collins (one of his favorites) to traditional and contemporary Hawaiian music. He also enjoyed opera, and following my mother's death, Hank was now left with an unused season ticket to Hawaii Opera Theater.

In the last years of Chip's life, he had the opportunity to get to know my new boyfriend, whom I'd started seeing in early 2010. When Paul and I traveled the first time together to Hawaii, Chip took a liking to him, giving him an uncharacteristically huge smile when they met. The next day, Chip looked at me, shaking his head in wonderment, and said, "I can't believe you brought Paul Simon to meet me!"

Paul did not miss a beat: "Chip, I'm not Paul Simon; my name is Paul Weinschenk. But Paul Simon and I are both short, old Jewish guys. And I'm flattered you think we look alike."

The end came quickly for Chip, and the shock was enormous. Thankfully, I was there for the brother for whom I had felt an intense love from the day he came into the world. The staff at Queens Medical Center in Honolulu were kind and compassionate and ensured that he did not suffer. Some of the wonderful doctors who had treated him over the years came to say their goodbyes. Hank and I also were there for each other, and my beautiful niece Gina flew in from Maui and helped me pick up Chip's few possessions from the group home where he'd been living. Again, all of these events were anticipated to some degree. But each was a drawn-out, wrenching experience that I buried in activity rather than taking the time I needed to reflect and heal.

At the same time, the personal and emotional depth of the intactivist cause was something I had never encountered at any time in my previous life. Taking on Intact America during this time, I realize now, both served to distract me from the losses and turmoil in my personal life and also deepened the meaning of those losses. Most importantly, the experience of leading IA—an organization created to dismantle a business that capitalizes on human suffering—also graced me with an opportunity to do something important that would make use of the gifts, lessons, relationships, and privileges I had the fortune of accruing throughout my life.

It wasn't until I began writing this memoir that I realized how poorly I had cared for myself during this difficult period. I also had to face how much the way my mother had prioritized intellect over emotion had rubbed off on me—in both good ways and bad.

Fortunately, despite all of the turmoil and less-than-excellent decisions on my part, I was able to continue earning a living. In 2005, I had founded a nonprofit company called the Hudson Center for Health Equity and Quality to develop and leverage some of the administrative streamlining products Hudson Health Plan needed. After the acquisition, I was able to return to my position as CEO of the Hudson Center and bring Intact America under that nonprofit umbrella. Subsequently, Intact America became a separate entity, but we still share office space and some administrative services with the Hudson Center, an arrangement that serves both organizations well.

Meanwhile, I added another few things to my plate—including working weekends in the gallery and gift shop attached to the glassblowing studio Paul started. (My son, in the meantime, had also become a glassblower.) As Intact America took on more employees and consultants and expanded programmatically, and as the time pressure of writing this book began to build, I moved away from the gallery and the relationship with Paul. We are now just neighbors, sharing two dogs and overlapping relationships with family members and friends. I am looking forward to the next stage of my intactivism, taking my book and the cause on the road and to the airwaves, while my talented young staff moves the organization forward.

Epilogue

OUR UNFINISHED BUSINESS

Circumcision is an astonishingly abusive practice. Yet this surgery serves as a baseline experience for most American boys and men and for those who love them. Cutting a child's genitals, the most intimate body parts, requires a willful suppression of empathy and compassion toward the smallest, most vulnerable members of the human race. Circumcision undermines the most basic imperatives of human survival—sexual pleasure designed for procreation and the human need for intimacy, and a mother's instinct to protect her children. Children thus damaged have been betrayed by the very adults charged with protecting their wellbeing. Circumcision cuts through us all.

I saw in the early days of my activism that nearly every mention of the word "circumcision" was fraught with discomfort and anxiety—the other person's and my own. With few exceptions, people simply did not want to talk about it. They didn't want to think about helpless babies being tied down and a knife taken to their penises—so they made jokes. Women didn't want to remember the way they felt when their baby was brought back to them, exhausted and traumatized after a surgery that had been promoted as "painless" or "just a snip." Men didn't want to think about being violated as babies, nor did they want to consider that

285

some of the problems they were facing now, decades later, might be due to this "minor" and "beneficial procedure" carried out on them without their consent. Consequently, they denied that it had affected them in any way.

Not until I took on the project of writing this book did I truly begin to understand—given most Americans' fight-or-flight response—how I got into this penis business and why I was perfectly suited for this important work.

As I set about answering my friend Lucie's question of why this cause, I became aware of how my unusual upbringing shaped my interest in this decidedly disruptive subject. Of course, witnessing the horror that resulted from my infant brother's circumcision was seared into my memory.

Drawing from my coming-of-age experiences in the 1960s at a time of cultural, political, and social change, a time when challenging the status quo was itself part of the status quo, I was barely fazed by the skepticism, criticism—even vilification—that intactivists confront as we stand up and defend the rights of baby boys.

I also realized that, for better or worse, being raised in a family that valued intellect over emotion had shaped the character of both my professional and personal relationships. For the most part, though not always, this upbringing served me well in my role as one of the leaders in the movement. .

I saw how the anthropological method I learned in my studies and field experience helped me to maintain distance as an observer, while repressing my own outrage and sorrow.

I appreciated how my traditional public health education gave me a set of analytical and quantitative tools, but also how a more radical political perspective gave me a framework to critique myriad public health efforts that exploit vulnerable people—the poor, the marginalized, people of color, and newborn babies—in the United States and elsewhere. My years of running a health plan taught me to manage and nurture an organization and engage with professional, government, and community stakeholders.

Finally, having the privilege of attending law school in my late 40s enabled me to see ways the legal system can be used both to perpetuate and to challenge the status quo, and how the study of law provides a window into our culture, offering both insights and tools for change.

But the lesson I had yet to learn would come over years of working in the intactivist movement and meeting and hearing from thousands of others who were—voluntarily or involuntarily (as victims)—impacted by circumcision: The physical, psychological and emotional harm done to a child harms everyone and impacts every relationship—both intimate and social—in that child's family and social constellation throughout that child's life. Infant male circumcision in our nation, the United States of America, cuts through us all.

As the founding executive director of Intact America, ensuring that the people and systems were in place to handle the work at hand, while at the same time navigating a world of human tragedy, was challenging and emotionally draining. Vetting and managing consultants; seeing to it that employee salaries and benefits were taken care of; making sure that our documents and correspondence were stored and secure; producing the monthly newsletter; seeking out and responding to interview opportunities; answering the ever-increasing volume of emails, phone calls, and postal correspondence—all these were things that in my previous life as CEO of a large organization, I could rely on staff for support. The health plan also—unlike Intact America —had a guaranteed source of revenue: patient care premiums paid by New York State. Now, as head of a new nonprofit organization advocating for a relatively unknown (and unpopular) cause, for the first time in my life I had to fundraise.

This new arena proved challenging to say the least. Dean Pisani's initial donation was given with the expectation that we would start big, make an impression, and build a significant donor base. To do this, we needed to look professional, with well-designed website, spiffy signage, and a business mailing address and telephone system (this was several years pre-pandemic and before the technology innovations that made remote work easier). We needed a public relations firm on retainer to field, pitch, and follow up on inquiries. We needed a professional Customer Relationship Management (CRM) platform, to recruit, track, and communicate with our constituents and donors.

Critically important, we needed to mount visible, meaningful programs to show the world we were not to be dismissed. Early on, I was taken aback to find that not every grassroots intactivist was on board with this new approach. In the early days of Intact America, I fielded criticism from a number of disgruntled individuals who thought that paying staff was wasteful; they believed that people who "really cared" should work "from the goodness their hearts"—in other words, for free. I disagreed.

While wholeheartedly supportive of our new organization, Marilyn Milos, the founder of our movement, who had always struggled with scarce and unpredictable donations, weighed in. On several occasions, she reminded me of her own philosophy: "The Universe will provide; it always has." Although she served as a key inspiration, on this point we diverged. Coming from a business background, I knew the enormous mission that we were tackling required money for staff and programs.

Initially, our newsletters, fundraising efforts, and other communications focused on debunking the myths supporting circumcision and highlighting the injustice and lack of ethics underlying the practice. Our attendance at large events such as Pride in New York City gave us the opportunity to talk about these issues, but over the years, we found it more effective and more engaging to pursue conversations about bodily autonomy.

At the same time, Intact America began conducting professional surveys designed to collect concrete data about the public's attitude toward circumcision and the intact penis. For more than a decade, we have been tracking the growing number of people in our country who accept the premise that boys should remain intact (indicating movement toward a tipping point). We attribute this change, in part, to the increased visibility of the intactivist movement, to our presence on social media, and to more online media coverage of the topic of circumcision.

But other surveys, including national and state-specific research about the frequency of circumcision solicitations (with results broken down by race), and about forcible retractions and ways the medical establishment undermines parents' inclinations to refuse the surgery, show that we still have a lot of work to do.

The generosity and confidence of Intact America donors has made it possible for our organization to maintain successful efforts, such as ongoing expansion of our social media presence, hosting booths at Pride events around the country, and continuing the tradition of the biannual conferences created by Marilyn in the early days of NoCirc. In addition, we have been able to launch new and exciting programs that we know will make a huge difference over time.

A lot of the ideas for our work come directly from our followers. In addition to communicating through the contact page on our website, or through comments on social media, people reach out to Intact America simply because they need to talk with someone about a past or recent trauma. IA's "Voices" feature, first published on our website and in monthly newsletters, was the first explicit effort to present first-person accounts from people who had been wronged by circumcision. Inevitably, these essays brought responses from readers with their own stories.

My personal mobile number can be found on the internet, and it's not unusual for me to receive a phone call in the early morning or late at night from a mom who is leaving the emergency room with her son after a doctor or nurse abruptly and brutally retracted his foreskin. Several of these mothers have told me that when they protested, the staff threatened to call security on them. Others reported that they were told that if they didn't themselves force back their sons' foreskins, they would be guilty of neglect.

Men write or call for advice on how to initiate conversations with their fathers, who are unwilling to hear or acknowledge the sons' deep grief over the wound that was inflicted on them decades earlier. Young men call to say that they are considering suicide and literally have no one with whom to share their suffering. And on occasion, I receive calls from family members struggling with a son's or spouse's despair. All these communications and experiences have helped shape Intact America's programmatic initiatives.

Survivors of infant circumcision have much in common with the victims of rape and sexual abuse carried out by prominent and powerful members of the establishment. As with these issues, circumcision stories have been repressed by the powers-that-be, and the shame and secrecy associated with the abuse have allowed the custom to continue, unchecked.

These insights have helped me to realize that everyone in the United States has a circumcision story, and that these stories are the most powerful weapon we have against continuation of this routine practice, so deeply ingrained in our culture. I know that the most valuable, tangible benefit Intact America can offer to our community is the opportunity for people to speak out. In this regard, Intact America has benefited considerably from the emergence of powerful new movements encouraging victims of assault and injustice to tell their stories and to confront their assailants publicly.

Reflecting this imperative, and in anticipation of releasing two memoirs (the one you are reading now, by me, and *Please Don't Cut the Baby*, by Marilyn Fayre Milos), Intact America began working on a major new campaign in in the spring and summer of 2023. Called *Skin in the Game* (skininthegame.org), the campaign consists of black and white photographic images of people of every race, ethnicity, sex, and body type who answered advertisements placed on social media inviting them to a photo shoot being held by a nonprofit organization called Intact America in Atlanta and Dallas. Those who expressed interest were offered a gift card for a nominal sum to help defray their travel expenses.

Over the course of the shoot, first IA staff members answered questions and spoke with the participants about their interest in the topic of circumcision. Then, photographer Kevin Garrett (whose creative vision sparked the project) further engaged the subjects in conversation about cutting babies' genitals, as he captured their emotional reactions on camera. Some of the male participants had been wounded significantly and had never talked to anyone about it. Among the women who joined us were partners of cut men, and mothers who deeply regretted allowing their sons to be cut. Each day served to confirm that, indeed, everyone has a circumcision story.

The reactions of those who participated in these photo shoots—from those who answered the call to IA staff, to photo crew, to IA supporters and consultants—were extraordinary. People who just a couple of hours earlier had been strangers were now sitting around a large table, eating the food we had prepared for the day, and talking quietly among themselves. Even after months of reviewing the photos and materials we are using for the campaign, the images from *Skin in the Game* bring tears to my eyes and pain in my heart. The Universe willing (thank you, Marilyn!), Intact America will take the campaign on the road, together with the memoirs, in the coming months and will publish an art book with the images and stories of the campaign participants.

Intact America also is on the cusp of signing off on a custom-developed consumer-facing electronic system called DoNoHarm.report. To be launched state-by-state beginning in the first half of 2024, DoNoHarm consists of standardized forms that will collect complaints from parents and others who were pressured by doctors or hospital personnel to cut their sons, or whose sons have experienced circumcision complications or who have been victims of forcible foreskin retraction.[56] The complaint system has no age restriction, so persons of any age who want to complain about their own circumcision or their son's circumcision can fill out a form. We ask for the name(s) of the perpetrator(s), the hospital or other facility where the violation took place, details of the event, and any other facts the complainant wishes to share.

DoNoHarm staff will help complainants to fill out the information and provide them with the printed forms and instructions on where to file (medical facilities, as well as state and national regulatory and quality-monitoring agencies). The system has been designed to automate—as much as possible—a process that for several years has been handled manually by Doctors Opposing Circumcision, IA's partner in the project. Our goal is—as finances permit—to promote DoNoHarm nationwide, and report regularly on the types and numbers of complaints collected and filed in each state, and the names of the responsible facilities and medical practices. Over time, we will be able—for the first time—to establish a record of circumcision complications and other abuses that the medical establishment has denied or ignored for decades.

Third, by popular demand and good fortune, we will be initiating an online, guided peer-group counseling program, moderated by psychotherapists who have interest and expertise in working with circumcision survivors. The program initially will be offered free-of-charge to a small group of IA newsletter subscribers and donors, and will expand as demand increases and as we are able to recruit more trained therapists.

The development of DoNoHarm.report, *Skin in the Game*, the online therapy program, and the production of this memoir together with Marilyn's *Please Don't Cut the Baby* were all made possible because of private donations from individuals who trust in Intact America's ability to execute meaningful and reputable programs. Every day I wake up and give thanks for the wonderful people I work with, to the intactivist community, and to donors who support our work. These include Dean Pisani, who placed his confidence in me on Day One; Gene Burkett who told me to "go for it" when he bequeathed his estate to Intact America; and the hundreds of individuals who reach out with their questions, their ideas, their donations, and their stories.

The gratitude these individuals have in turn expressed to me, and to Intact America, reflects—in addition to confidence in the organization—a sense of enormous relief that they are not alone; the belief that sharing their stories is the first step in shedding the shame and stigma many have carried for a lifetime; and the knowledge that this is the path to liberating us all from the burden of living in a society that practices routine child genital cutting.

I know we are moving toward a tipping point. Among the reasons for my optimism is *you*, the person reading this book. Whether you're a part of the movement, or you picked it up because the title was weird, the fact that you've read to the end means that you understand: cutting a child's genitals is wrong and that it must stop. But you also know by now that no cause is won simply because it is just. If being right were all it takes, then "routine" infant circumcision—a morally bankrupt, perverted attack on children—would never have begun or would have fizzled long ago.

So, if you're wondering right now what YOU can do to bring about the demise of the penis business, the words that follow are for you.

First, if you haven't done so already, sign up for news from Intact America at www.intactamerica.org and follow us on social media platforms. This way, you'll always be up-to-date on our activities. And you can find opportunities to share your story and engage with others, online and in person.

Second, speak out, starting today! Don't be intimidated by those who try to defend the penis business in a last-ditch effort to keep people from learning the truth. Think about the incredibly powerful MeToo movement. The key contribution of its founder Tarana Burke was to recognize that every victim's story deserves recognition, that every person, regardless of their gender, color, race, sexuality, or economic status, is entitled to be heard. You are entitled to be heard. Speaking your truth will set you free.

Third, don't feel you need to master "the science" before having the right to say that cutting a baby's genitals is wrong. Nobody needs to read medical journal articles to call BS when a medical "expert" on TV tells them that boys can't learn to wash their penises or that inflicting an open wound on a baby's genitals is cleaner than bathing him in warm water. If you're a man who has been cut and hates it, you don't need facts and figures to declare, "I hate what was done to me." If you're a parent, you don't need to know any "science" to say, "I was duped into letting a stranger amputate part of my son's penis." And if you are the loved one of a boy or man who is suffering from the consequences of genital mutilation, help that person to heal by listening and empathizing, and encourage him to share his story.

Fourth, if you have been harmed, complain! And encourage others to complain. Tell everyone you know about DoNoHarm.report. We haven't put an age limit on reporting circumcision solicitations, circumcision injuries, and forcible retraction incidents, so adult men who were violated decades ago can still file.

I know that once your heart has been touched, there's no turning back. Change might be slow at first, but once we hit that all important tipping point—when a quarter of the population accepts that an intact penis is a normal penis—circumcision will begin to die out. Cut men will, at the least, know that the cycle of wounding and trauma has come to an end and that future boys will be spared. In a post-genital-cutting era, even as doctors and other medical professionals scramble to disavow their participation, those who have engaged in the practice will never be able to escape the truth about the damage they have caused.

As you read these words, you may be thinking of conversations you've already had—perhaps even since you've began reading this book. If you are feeling uncomfortable, I can assure you that as time goes on, you'll find your story and your voice. You will come up with your own responses from your common sense and from your heart, and you'll refine them over time as you see what works best. You'll also find, as I have, that some of the people who protest the most when they first hear your message will come back to you later and say, "You know, I've been thinking about it. You're right." And then, more often than not, *they* do have a story:

- *My husband isn't circumcised. I have no idea why we didn't talk about it before letting them do that to our son.*
- *I thought my parents would be mad when I brought it up. But my mother told me my bris was the worst day of her life.*
- *After talking with you, I went home and apologized to my son.*
- *I just realized the problems my husband and I are having in bed probably come from his circumcision. I'm still angry, but now it's at the people who did that to him.*

Nearly always, your best response to such comments is to say, "Thank you for sharing that with me. You're not alone because—sadly—circumcision cuts through us all."

Nothing could have prepared me for Jonathon Conte's death by suicide, only days after he rode smiling through Golden Gate Park on his bicycle, pulling a cart with signs proclaiming, "Protect All Children from Genital Mutilation," and "Foreskin Is Fabulous!"[57] Or for the inconsolable grief of Lesley Roberts, whose son took his own life after being sold a circumcision by a doctor when he was age 23.[58] Or the pain and suffering of a Florida mother whose young son, in despair, ended his life after his father refused to acknowledge his suffering.

But change is happening. I have met many men who thought their lives were over when they discovered the truth about what had been done to their bodies. By getting involved, though, by sharing their stories and hearing from others who have survived, they have found that it's possible to heal, to love and be loved, and to help others to overcome.

As the impact of Intact America and intactivism grows, I keep thinking of the advice Cecile Richards, activist and past president of Planned Parenthood, offers in her memoir *Make Trouble*. She credits it to Warren Buffett: "[N]ever shy away from telling people what you do. You dispel myths, for others and yourself."

This book is my story. It has helped liberate me from some of the pain I have felt, and the myths I've subscribed to, over my lifetime. Furthermore, Richards says: "Know that there's no road map for social change—so keep making it up, don't get stuck or tied down, and never turn down a new opportunity."[59] I'll take all that to heart!

People can change. People do change. And if we view our detractors not as enemies, but as "those who have yet to come along," that optimism, that inclusivity, will move us forward.

My everyday coffee mug features a quote similar to one attributed to Mahatma Gandhi. Nicholas Klein, head of the Amalgamated Clothing Workers of America, said in a speech in 1914, "First they ignore you. Then they ridicule you. Then they attack you and want to burn you. And then they build monuments to you."

I'll meet you at the monument.

ACKNOWLEDGMENTS AND GRATEFUL MENTIONS

I have been writing this memoir for sixty years. I have been watching events as they unfolded and listening to the reactions and stories of people who, like me, observed them, participated in them, and discussed them, as well as those who denied their occurrence. My first impulse was to include everyone who has contributed to my thinking, my knowledge, and my feelings about the American medical establishment's penchant for amputating part of every boy's penis. But many of these people appear in the pages of this memoir, and I have decided to let these appearances serve as tributes to their importance in my evolution from observer to analyst to activist.

Here, I want to recognize those who have contributed most directly to the conceiving, shaping, and writing of this book.

In constructing an account of one's life and experiences, where does one go for details and corroboration beyond the memories and muddle in one's own head? Although many of those who appear here are no longer living, I am fortunate to have several people in my life today who (though they bear no responsibility for my opinions and conclusions) have helped me significantly to sort out some of that muddle.

First, my sister Julia, three years younger than me, and the person I have known longer than anyone else on the planet. While sifting through memories, when I found myself confused about details or timelines, the name of a short-lived pet, events that occurred during our growing-up years, I consulted my sister. Most of her recollections went beyond my initial question, leading to conversations—some revelatory, many humorous—between the two of us that, but for this book, would have gone unexplored.

Second, Hank Chapin, the father who raised me since I was eight years old. I credit my expansive interests in part to Hank's ecumenical and voracious reading habits. He also taught me that an author need not be great or famous to be readable and enjoyable. Fortunately, Hank also has a broad recall of events in our family life, as well as his unique and somewhat curious observations about many peripheral but relevant people and events. As I neared completion of this manuscript, during a dinnertime conversation among Julia, me, our brother Nick, and Hank, the latter posed a riddle: "What are the six most terrifying words in the English language?" We all looked at each other and then, expectantly, at Hank. The answer: "My daughter is writing a memoir." Dear Dad, thank you for everything supportive, provocative, and brave that we have touched upon in the past 63 years.

Third, my Yellow Springs High School classmates. As improbable as it may seem given that I have returned to Yellow Springs only a handful of times in the past 50 years, I still treasure my experiences from high school—1965-1969. As word of my involvement in the intactivist cause made it around the internet, a number of my high school classmates have gone out of their way to tell me how inspired they are by my work to protect boys, and that they look forward to reading my book. At a time when so many otherwise reasonable people are still embarrassed by the topic, or afraid to look me in the eye, this is remarkable, and is *so* Yellow Springs. Thank you all, especially Pete Bush and Lisa Babbage Jackson.

Fourth, Davida Scharf, who became my friend the day we arrived at Barnard College in fall 1969. Our conversations about circumcision go back 45 years, to the birth of Davida's first child. Of the same vintage, though not a college classmate, is my steadfast friend Henry Ehrlich, who wrote the first book about adoption I ever read, and who has been a cheerleader for all my work over the decades.

Next, my dear friend Irene Dillon who, from the moment I mentioned writing this memoir, has been an unwavering source of encouragement, substantive suggestions, pet photos, snide commentary, and good cheer.

Sheilah McGlone, RN, one of the kindest people I know.

Jasper Reid. We met in the 1990s in the world of health care consulting, and slowly discovered a shared history and common interests in literature, language, and humanity. Jasper has been a unique source of insights and support during the time it took me to write this book.

Finally, my colleagues and beloved friends from the intactivist movement who have so selflessly and patiently collaborated over the decades, putting aside small differences among us in order to fight for the rights of boys to their intact bodies.

Marilyn Milos, "mother of the movement" and world expert on all matters foreskin, for the sacrifices she has made, her mastery of detail, and her over-the-top endorsements of my work. The latter are exceeded in number only by Marilyn's apologies for "getting" me into leading Intact America. Marilyn is author of *Please Don't Cut the Baby: A Nurse's Memoir*, released simultaneously with *This Penis Business*.

Dean Edell, MD, who, after seeing me on a *Today Show* interview conducted in a bare-bones studio in Washington, DC, wrote with some useful advice: "Never go anywhere without a compact of translucent face powder in your bag."

The intellectual leaders of the intactivist movement, especially Leonard Glick, scholar, humanist, husband of the wonderful Nansi Glick, and a source of great wisdom. I'll never forget Len's advice when I consulted him about an intra-movement controversy: "Let them squabble. You and Intact America, just stick to your knitting." And Brian Earp, whose wide-ranging intellectual explorations have taken the movement to new levels of discourse and understanding.

My intactivist lawyer buddies, especially John Geisheker, Steven Svoboda, David Wilton, and David Llewellyn.

Other colleagues whose availability and willingness to explore the American penis business have deepened my own analysis and commitment to fighting it: Shelton Walden, Rebecca Wald, Lisa Braver Moss, Robert Johnson, William Kaye, Tora Spigner, Ruthie Fraser, Alexandro José Gradilla.

Writers who have inspired me to write in the memoir mode, including Frederick Buechner (my sister-in-law Katherine Arthaud's father), and others whom I never met but whose personal stories have illuminated the passion underlying their righteous causes. To name a very few: Frederick Douglass (three autobiographies, especially *My Bondage and My Freedom*); John Lewis (*Walking with the Wind: A Memoir of the Movement*); Willie Parker, MD (*Life's Work: A Moral Argument for Choice*); Sonia Sotomayor (*My Beloved World*); Cecile Richards (*Make Trouble*); and Angela Tucker (*You Should be Grateful*, about interracial adoption from the adoptee's perspective).

Tarana Burke, founder of the MeToo movement. And, of course, the late Harvey (*I'm here to recruit you*) Milk.

Family members and friends who have supported Intact America's mission and taken an interest in my work: Ernesto Echeverria, Julia Bozzo, David Chapin, Parker Chapin, Marj Chapin and Jean Parker, Katherine Buechner Arthaud, Betsy Pattullo, Martha Roth and Bill

Irwin, Paul Arthaud, Don Hall, Sherry Rohlfing, Sherri Ehrlich, Paula Garcia-Zuazua, Rio Cruz, Nikolaos Robakis, Davida Scharf, Katherine Weinschenk, and Pablo (Paul) Weinschenk.

My Woodstock friends, artists Margie Greve and Jackie Oster, writer and massage therapist Julie Evans. And Seth Levine who, remarkably, has managed to make weight-training into entertainment.

Intact America board members and donors: Dan Bollinger, Chris Maurer, Kevin Nelson, and Marilyn Milos. Supporting staff from the Hudson Center, including Marisel Stuck, Sherri Ehrlich, and Howard Birnbaum.

Founding and sustaining donor to Intact America, Dean Pisani, kind, intelligent, and rock-solid in his support and patience over the years. Legacy donor Gene Burkett, who passed away in 2020. Dean and Gene, your confidence in my judgment and ability to lead this organization and this movement have made possible programs and efforts that were only a pipedream before Intact America.

Other donors and volunteers too numerous to mention: every single one of you is making a difference. Thank you, thank you, thank you.

Alan Cumming, whom I credit for thinking I could produce a book about circumcision a decade ago and to whom I owe a hundred apologies for not completing it then.

Every medical and nursing practitioner who refuses to cut or participate in the cutting of babies' genitals. A special shout-out to physicians Steve Dorfman, Kenneth Zatz, and James Verrees. Every doula and nurse who tells moms the truth about circumcision. John Jacoby, MD, who teases me but knows I'm right.

Intact America's awesome and trustworthy consultants and advisors: Sue Sena, Bonnie Catena, Sally Parker, Robin Laverne (Dragonfly) Wilson, and Tora Spigner.

Jeannie Ashford, who began as "our PR person," at Hudson Health Plan, and who over two decades has become my confidante, trusted advisor, and advocate for Intact America's work and principles. When I asked Jeannie's advice on finding a co-writer to help me produce my memoir, she introduced me to Echo Garrett.

Echo Montgomery Garrett, my co-writer, editor, publisher, motivator, and sharer of personal intimacies and rather extraordinary coincidences—the latter too numerous to list (except for Texas, Albuquerque, and missing out on the Lady Macbeth role and being relegated, instead, to playing a witch). Echo knew when to listen, when to advise, when to reset, when to commiserate, and helped me all along to strike a balance between the painful, the poignant, and the provocative, and to eliminate the probably irrelevant.

Judith Kirkwood, talented editor and lovely all-around person. Judy reviewed several "final" drafts of this book, shortened my absurdly long sentences and, together with Echo, improved my story and message immeasurably. All of that said, any awkward phrases or grammatical and factual errors are mine alone.

Kevin Garrett, photographer. As I was wrapping up the writing of this book, Kevin conceived of the photo project to support Intact America's new, overarching campaign, called *Skin in the Game: Circumcision Cuts through Us All*. His artistic vision has resulted in a series of astonishingly powerful images that will power Intact America's work to new levels. My thanks also to Ken Schneiderman, Ray Hardy, Stephen Mancuso, and the supporting crew members in both Atlanta and Dallas, who created an

304 This Penis Business: A Memoir

unequivocally welcoming environment for three photoshoots, complete with food, conversation, and compassion.

Kelly Floyd, whom we were fortunate to recruit after her extraordinary presentation at Intact 2022, did an extraordinary job managing the photoshoot participants, as well as expertly and compassionately interviewing (along with Echo Garrett) dozens of people about their feelings and experiences related to male genital cutting.

Sergio Serratto, who helped with translations and outreach to the Latino community.

A separate thank you goes to Echo and Kevin Garrett for welcoming me into their home for extended periods of time, sharing their cats Isabella and Salvador with me when I was missing my own pets, introducing me to some of Atlanta's culinary highlights, and so generously sharing their commitment to and creative vision for dismantling the penis business.

Words are inadequate to express my thanks to Dan Bollinger, who has contributed immeasurably to the work of Intact America since our founding in 2008. For the past 15 years, I've relied on Dan, a great record-keeper, indefatigable researcher, and (usually) patient critic, for brains, strategy, and his ability to produce a document or citation within minutes and with minimal judgment and grumbling. My thanks, also, to Dan's wife Rebecca, whose good humor has endured despite interrupted meals and movies when I call to (re)check a fact, or (re)hash an evolving position or strategy.

Similarly, my deepest appreciation for Stephen Patterson, who came to work at Intact America as a summer intern, who returned after receiving his communications degree and who, while growing into his current position as IA's deputy director, has helped to shape every aspect of our organization's evolution. With his (usually) reserved demeanor, I can count on Stephen to listen to my ideas, sincerely attempt to read my mind, reflect before responding, and then politely reframe or redirect the discussion to suggest the best possible outcomes. Stephen's kindness and wisdom are also in evidence when dealing with the most personal and intimate issues of Intact America's constituents and others who reach out to us for advice and help.

Finally, my profound gratitude to the hundreds of men and women who have shared their personal stories with me—survivors of male genital cutting, "regret mothers" and fathers of boys who have been cut, parents who have resisted the pressure placed on them by a runaway medical system—and the many, many more who are now speaking out, telling your truths so that others will be spared.

Georganne Chapin
West Hurley, NY

ABOUT THE AUTHORS

Georganne Chapin is a healthcare expert, attorney, social justice advocate, and founding executive director of Intact America, the nation's most influential organization opposing the U.S. medical industry's common practice of surgically altering ("circumcising") the genitals of male children.

Growing up with socially aware, college professor parents, exposed to people from many backgrounds, and motivated by an innate sense of justice, Georganne received a BA in Anthropology, *magna cum laude*, from Barnard College, and a Master's degree in Sociomedical Sciences from Columbia University. For 25 years, she served as chief executive officer of Hudson Health Plan, one of New York's original Medicaid managed care organizations, taking the award-winning nonprofit insurer from a few hundred patients and a handful of staff members in 1989, to 150,000 patients, nearly 350 employees, and annual revenue of nearly $800 million when the company was acquired in 2014. She also founded the nonprofit Hudson Center for Health Equity and Quality, a company that creates software and provides consulting services designed to reduce administrative complexities, streamline and integrate data collection and reporting, and enhance access to healthcare for those in need.

When mid-career Georganne enrolled in an evening program at Pace University School of Law, she set about to explore the legal, ethical, and cultural issues underlying routine male circumcision, a subject that had interested her since witnessing the traumatic aftermath of the surgery conducted on her younger brother. In 2004, she graduated from Pace *cum laude*, with certificates in Health Law and International Law. Following her graduation, she taught Bioethics and Medicaid and Disability Law at Pace, and Bioethics in Dominican College's doctoral program for advanced practice nurses.

Mentored by pioneers in the intactivist (anti-circumcision) movement, in 2008, Chapin co-founded Intact America, a nonprofit organization dedicated to protecting boys from the routine amputation of their normal penile foreskins. Under her leadership, Intact America has become the leading voice defending the rights of all children to be free from medically unnecessary genital surgery to which they cannot consent. In addition, Intact America's nationwide surveys have definitively documented tactics used by U.S. doctors and healthcare facilities to pathologize the male foreskin, pressure parents into circumcising their sons, and forcibly retract the foreskins of intact boys—all of this creating potentially lifelong, iatrogenic harm.

Chapin has published many articles and op-ed essays and has been interviewed widely on local, national and international television, radio and podcasts about ways the U.S. healthcare system exploits vulnerable patients, prioritizing profits over people's basic healthcare needs. She cites routine, non-therapeutic infant circumcision as a glaring example of a practice that wastes money, harms boys and the men they will become, and compromises the well-being of their family members and intimate partners. *This Penis Business: A Memoir* is her first book.

Journalist **Echo Montgomery Garrett** has spent her career finding and writing stories that matter. From the moment she and **Georganne Chapin** first spoke about "this penis business," Echo knew this project was a social justice issue that had the potential to change millions of lives. As the mother of two sons, she had questioned the routine practice of circumcision when they were born but couldn't find anyone among her peers who had not had their sons cut. She later joined the sisterhood of regret moms, who were pressured by medical professionals to circumcise, and has since dedicated herself to getting the truth about this medically bogus surgery that irreversibly harms boys and the men they will become into the American public's conscience.

A graduate of Auburn University, Echo has co-authored, contributed to, or ghostwritten twenty-five nonfiction books, including *Why Don't They Just Get a Job: One Couple's Mission to End Poverty in their Community*, by Liane Phillips, which won the Independent Book Publishers Association Benjamin Franklin Award in the Social Issues category. Liane and her husband Dave, co-founded Cincinnati Works, an award-winning nonprofit.

Echo also co-authored with Sam Bracken *My Orange Duffel Bag: A Journey to Radical Change*. She co-founded the Orange Duffel Bag Initiative (ODBI), a nonprofit that provides life plan coaching and ongoing advocacy to young people ages 14-24, who are experiencing poverty, homelessness or aging out of foster care. The book won two international awards for best book design, and five awards for best young adult non-fiction and best self-help, including the American Society of Journalist and Authors *Arlene Eisenberg Award for Writing that Makes a Difference.*

Echo is co-founder (with her son Connor Judson Garrett) and CEO of Lucid House Publishing, LLC, publisher of both This Penis Business and Marilyn Milos's *Please Don't Cut the Baby!* She and her husband Kevin Garrett, who photographed the *Skin in the Game: Circumcision Cuts Through Us All* campaign, reside in Marietta, Georgia.

NOTES

PREFACE

1. "A remedy which is almost always successful in small boys is circumcision....The operation should be performed by a surgeon without administering an anesthetic, as the brief pain attending the operation will have a salutary effect upon the mind....In females, the author has found the application of pure carbolic acid to the clitoris an excellent means of allaying the abnormal excitement."
   - Dr. John Harvey Kellogg
   Cited in David L. Gollaher, *Circumcision: A History of the World's Most Controversial Surgery* (New York: Basic Books, 2000), p. 103.

CHAPTER 4

2. Bob Kraus, "Bill Kea? Oh, he was one real *kolohe* [rascal] kid," *Honolulu Advertiser*, Nov. 24, 2002.

CHAPTER 6

3. Meatal stenosis, narrowing of the urethral opening, is a condition that almost exclusively affects circumcised boys or men. It can cause painful, prolonged and frequent urination, as well as an inability to aim the urine stream or empty the bladder. Meatal stenosis is linked to circumcision due to the injury caused to the penis as a result of being cut. The glans suffers from irritation as a result of being exposed to diapers and clothing, and the scar tissue that forms around the meatus obstructs the flow of urine. Meatal stenosis may

also occur as a result of lack of blood flow to the circumcised penis, or build-up of uric acid and ammonia crystals which—over time—cause prolonged inflammation and a narrowed meatus. Studies suggest meatal stenosis may occur in as many as 1 out of every 5 circumcised males.

Smail Acimi et al. "Prevalence and Causes of Meatal Stenosis in Circumcised Boys." *Journal of Pediatric Urology,* 2022 Feb;18(1):89. e1-89.e6. doi: 10.1016/j.jpurol.2021.10.008. Epub 2021 Oct 20; https://pubmed.ncbi.nlm.nih.gov/34740536/.

CHAPTER 8

4. Ann Fessler, *The Girls Who Went Away: The Hidden History of Women Who Surrendered Children for Adoption in the Years before Roe v. Wade* (New York: Penguin, 2006).

CHAPTER 10

5. Antioch College disbanded Unity House in 1970, after the Department of Health, Education and Welfare criticized the facility for violating the federal Civil Rights Act by "limiting itself to Negro students only...." *The New York Times*, Feb. 1, 1970.

CHAPTER 15

6. https://queenseagle.com/all/queens-based-inkarayku-brings-andean-arts-and-culture-to-beat-of-the-boroughs.

CHAPTER 31

7. Dan Bollinger and Georganne Chapin, "Child Genital Cutting as an Adverse Childhood Experience." White Paper, 2019.

http://adversechildhoodexperiences.net/CGC_as_an_ACE.pdf.

8. For an exhaustive, textbook treatment of bioethics, *see* Tom L. Beauchamp and James F. Childress, *Principles of Biomedical Ethics* (Oxford, UK: Oxford University Press, 8th edition, 2019). For a discussion about the bioethical principles implicated in routine infant circumcision, see Doctors Opposing Circumcision, "Medical Ethics and the Non-therapeutic Circumcision of Male Children." Seattle, WA. June 2016; updated August 2020. https://www. doctorsopposingcircumcision.org/for-professionals/medical-ethics/.

CHAPTER 32

9. Throughout history, there have been Jews who have foregone circumcision for their sons. Today, many secular U.S. Jews have their newborn sons' foreskins removed by doctors in hospitals (a procedure that has no ritual significance), and increasing numbers are simply choosing to keep their sons intact. Those who wish for a traditional welcoming ceremony now can choose an alternative known as brit shalom ("covenant of peace" in Hebrew), as opposed to brit milah ("covenant of circumcision").

"Brit shalom is an uplifting, celebratory baby-naming ceremony specifically designed for non-circumcising families. It's an affirmation that despite what may be seen by others as a radical choice, the family still considers themselves to be Jewish. And it's a beautiful symbolic acknowledgment of the ancient Abrahamic covenant."

One of the earliest such ceremonies was officiated by Rabbi Nathan Segal (1949-2019) in the mid-1980s. The movement grew from

there. Today, "many progressive rabbis, such as those from the Reform movement, will officiate if asked."
Lisa Braver Moss & Rebecca Wald, "Do You Know about Brit Shalom," Oct.15, 2021.
https://intactamerica.org/dyk_about-brit-shalom/

CHAPTER 33

10. RVU stands for "relative value unit," assigned by the federal government to each of more than 10,000 procedure codes and used by almost all health insurers to determine how much a doctor will get paid for a particular procedure. The elements of an RVU are physician work (the relative level of time, skill, training and intensity to provide a given service), practice expense (the costs of maintaining a practice, including rent, equipment, supplies and nonphysician staff costs), and "malpractice (the cost of professional liability insurance). Wikipedia, "Relative Value Unit." https://en.wikipedia.org/wiki/Relative_value_unit.
Quote is from personal communication from J. to author, April 20, 2023.

11. Personal communication with Tora Spigner, April 15, 2022.

12. American Academy of Pediatrics, Committee on Fetus and Newborn. *Standards and Recommendation for Hospital Care of Newborn Infants.* 5th ed. Evanston, IL: American Academy of Pediatrics, 1971:110. https://www.cirp.org/library/statements/aap/

13. David Gollaher reviews the shifting and ambiguous positions on circumcision taken by the American Academy of Pediatrics from the 1970s through the 1990s in *Circumcision: A History of the*

World's Most Controversial Surgery (New York: Basic Books, 2000), pp. 168-172.

14. American Academy of Pediatrics, March 1, 1999, "Circumcision Policy Statement, Task Force on Circumcision." *Pediatrics* (1999) 103 (3): 686–693.

https://doi.org/10.1542/peds.103.3.686.

CHAPTER 34

15. In comparing female genital cutting to newborn male genital cutting, the Bioethics committee said: "The American Academy of Pediatrics policy statement on newborn male circumcision expresses respect for parental decision-making and acknowledges the legitimacy of including cultural, religious, and ethnic traditions when making the choice of whether to surgically alter a male infant's genitals. Of course, parental decision-making is not without limits, and pediatricians must always resist decisions that are likely to cause harm to children. Most forms of FGC are decidedly harmful, and pediatricians should decline to perform them, even in the absence of any legal constraints. However, the ritual nick suggested by some pediatricians is not physically harmful and is much less extensive than routine newborn male genital cutting. "There is reason to believe that offering such a compromise may ...build trust between hospitals and immigrant communities, save some girls from undergoing disfiguring and life-threatening procedures in their native countries, and play a role in the eventual eradication of FGC. It might be more effective if federal and state laws enabled pediatricians to reach out to families by offering a ritual nick as a possible compromise to avoid greater harm."

American Academy of Pediatrics, Committee on Bioethics, "Policy Statement—Ritual Genital Cutting of Female Minors," *Pediatrics*; originally published online April 26, 2010; DOI: 10.1542/peds.2010-0187. p. 1093.

16. Norah MacReady, "AAP Retracts Statement on Controversial Procedure," *The Lancet* 376, 9734: 15, July 3, 2010.

17. American Academy of Pediatrics, Task Force on Male Circumcision, "Technical Report: Male Circumcision," *Pediatrics*, 130, 3, September 2012. Citations that follow are from the electronic version, pp. e756-85. www.pediatrics.org/cgi/doi/10.1542/peds.2012-1990.

18. Ibid.

19. AAP 2012 Task Force Report, p. e778.

20. AAP 2012 Task Force Report, p. e772.

21. AAP 2012 Task Force Report, p. e775.

22. "The literature review does not support the belief that male circumcision adversely affects penile sexual function or sensitivity, or sexual satisfaction, regardless of how these factors are defined. Sexual Satisfaction and Sensitivity Literature since 1995 includes 2 good quality randomized controlled trials that evaluated the effect of adult circumcision on sexual satisfaction and sensitivity in Uganda and Kenya, respectively. Among 5000 Ugandan participants, circumcised men reported significantly less pain on intercourse than uncircumcised men. At 2 years' postcircumcision, sexual satisfaction had increased significantly from baseline measures in the control group (from 98% at baseline to 99.9%); satisfaction levels remained stable among the circumcised men (98.5% at baseline, 98.4% 2 years

after the procedure). This study included no measures of time to ejaculation or sensory changes on the penis.

"In the Kenyan study (which had a nearly identical design and similar results), 64% of circumcised men reported much greater penile sensitivity postcircumcision. At the 2-year followup, 55% of circumcised men reported having an easier time reaching orgasm than they had precircumcision, although the findings did not reach statistical significance..."

American Academy of Pediatrics 2012 Task Force Report, p. e769.

23. https://publications.aap.org/pediatrics/article/130/3/585/30235/Circumcision-Policy-Statement

CHAPTER 35

24. Dan Bollinger, "Lost Boys: An Estimate of U.S. Circumcision-Related Infant Deaths, *Thymos: Journal of Boyhood Studies*, 4, 1, Spring 2010, pp. 78-90.

25. https://www.kqed.org/forum/201208290900/circumcision-benefits-said-to-outweigh-risks. Comment at 12:21 in recording.

26. https://www.kqed.org/forum/201208290900/circumcision-benefits-said-to-outweigh-risks. Comment at 12:40 in recording.

27. https://nypost.com/2011/05/05/tots-shock-hosp-death/.

28. https://nationalpost.com/health/ontario-newborn-bleeds-to-death-after-family-doctor-persuades-parents-to-get-him-circumcised.

29. Personal email from John Heydari to author, July 10, 2017.

CHAPTER 36

30. In 2019, the journal *Pediatrics* published a study which confirmed that circumcised newborns at 3 days old are more likely to struggle

with breastfeeding than their genitally intact siblings. These were the results: "Breastfeeding duration was lower for circumcised infants than for sibling controls....Circumcised infants were less likely to breastfed for 4-6 months...and less likely to breastfeed for at least 6 months. Conclusion: Early circumcision, within the first 3 days of life, may have a negative effect on the duration of breastfeeding. In our study, circumcised male infants had more than 4 fewer weeks of breastfeeding than their sibling controls." April Tan, Lawrence Noble, Samhita Jain, Alice Shajan, Diego Craik, "The Effect of Early Circumcision on Breastfeeding Duration Using Sibling Comparisons," *Pediatrics* August 2019; 144 (2_ MeetingAbstract): 273. 10.1542/peds.144.2MA3.273

31. Lesley Roberts, *A Is for Alex: A Bereaved Mother's Promise to her Beloved Son* (Cherish Editions: 2021).

32. Confidential communication to the author from a family member.

CHAPTER 37

33. http://www.cirp.org/library/cultural/maimonides/

34. Ibid.

35. Jon D. Levenson, "The New Enemies of Circumcision," *Commentary*, March 2000. https://www.commentary.org/articles/ jon-levenson-2/the-new-enemies-of-circumcision/

36. Dan Bollinger and Robert Van Howe, "Alexithymia and Circumcision Trauma: A Preliminary Investigation," *International Journal of Men's Health*, 10, 2, Summer 2011: 184-195. Also see, Dan Bollinger, "Adding Insult to Injury: Acquisition of Erectile Dysfunction from Circumcision." Research Gate Publication No.

322056383, March 2014, rev'd 2016. https://www.researchgate.net/publication/322056383

37. Curiosity with John and Mike, Episode 86 | Georganne Chapin | Intact America (Opposing Circumcision). August 3, 2022. https://podcasts.apple.com/us/podcast/episode-86-georganne-chapin-intact-america-opposing/id1549432889?i=1000574553369. Also available on Intact America's YouTube channel: https://www.youtube.com/watch?v=4njJ5uCa3Uo

CHAPTER 38

38. Pew Research Center, "Jewish Americans in 2020," May 11, 2021. https://www.pewresearch.org/religion/2021/05/11/the-size-of-the-u-s-jewish-population/

CHAPTER 39

39. https://health.costhelper.com/circumcision.html

40. Dan Bollinger, "Adding Insult to Injury. Acquisition of Erectile Dysfunction from Circumcision." https://www.researchgate.net/publication/322056383_Adding_Insult_to_Injury_Acquisition_of_Erectile_Dysfunction_from_Circumcision

41. Dan Bollinger, "High Cost of Circumcision, 5.7 Billion Annually." https://www.researchgate.net/publication/350709776_High_Cost_of_Circumcision_57_Billion_Annually.

42. https://fashionmagazine.com/beauty-grooming/today-in-really-really-weird-beauty-news-oprahs-favourite-moisturizer-is-made-from-human-foreskins/

43. "Sandra Bullock Got a 'Penis Facial'." https://www.youtube.com/watch?v=BY2aOHQlAco

44. https://www.lifelinecelltech.com/shop/tissue-type/skin-tissue/human-epidermal-keratinocytes-neonatal-fc-0007/

45. https://www.amazon.com/106-05N-Neonatal-Foreskin-Fibroblasts-Applications/dp/B07329SPHN/ref=cm_cr_arp_d_product_top?ie=UTF8.

46. Molly Glick, "Why human foreskin is a hot commodity in science," *Discover*, July 26, 2021. https://www.discovermagazine.com/the-sciences/why-human-foreskin-is-a-hot-commodity-in-science.

47. For a general discussion about the language that has evolved to justify current practices surrounding human tissue "donation," see Michael A. Lensink et al, "Better governance starts with better words: why responsible human tissue research demands a change of language." BMC Medical Ethics 23, Article number: 90 (2022) .

CHAPTER 40

48. https://www.ncbi.nlm.nih.gov/pmc/articles/PMC9576047/#:~:text=Circumcision%2C%20the%20surgical%20removal%20of,men%20are%20circumcised%20%5B2%5D.

49. Edward Wallerstein, *Circumcision: An American Health Fallacy* (Springer: New York, 1980), p. 17.

50. P.C. Remondino MD, "Questions of the day: Negro rapes and their social problems," *National Popular Review*, Vol. 4, January 1894, pp. 3-6. Remondino's book about circumcision, written in 1891, is still available through Amazon, as well as online. See P.C. Remondino, MD, *History of Circumcision from the Earliest Times to the Present: Moral and Physical Reasons for its Performance, with a History of Eunichism, Hermaphrodism, etc., and of the Different*

Operations Practiced upon the Prepuce. https://www.gutenberg.org/files/23135/23135-h/23135-h.htm.

CHAPTER 41

51. MSNBC Segment on Circumcision with Georganne Chapin of Intact America, 2009.
https://www.youtube.com/watch?v=aiV75vzS4To.

52. For a recent critique of the failure of Voluntary Medical Male Circumcision to curb the transmission of HIV in sub-Saharan African countries, see Luseno, W.K., Rennie, S. & Gilbertson, A. "A review of public health, social and ethical implications of voluntary medical male circumcision programs for HIV prevention in sub-Saharan Africa." *Int J Impot Res* 35, 269–278 (2023).
https://doi.org/10.1038/s41443-021-00484-x.

Abstract: "Ideally, the benefits of public health interventions should outweigh any associated harms, burdens, and adverse unintended consequences. The intended benefit of voluntary medical male circumcision (VMMC) programs in eastern and southern Africa (ESA) is the reduction of HIV infections. We review the literature for evidence of reductions in HIV incidence, evaluate the extent to which decreases in HIV incidence can be reasonably attributed to VMMC programs, and summarize social harms and ethical concerns associated with these programs. Review findings suggest that HIV incidence had been declining across ESA since before the large-scale rollout of VMMC as a public health intervention, and that this decline may be due to the combined effects of HIV prevention and treatment interventions, such as expanded antiretroviral therapy. The independent effect of VMMC programs in reducing HIV infections at the population level remains unknown. On the other hand, VMMC-associated evidence is increasing for the existence of negative social impacts such as stigmatization and/or discrimination, and ethically problematic practices, including lack of informed consent. We conclude that the relationship between the benefits and burdens of VMMC programs may be more unfavorable than what has been commonly suggested by proponents of global VMMC campaigns."

53. *See* Eugene T. Richardson, E*pidemic Illusions: On the Coloniality of Global Public Health* (Cambridge, MA: MIT Press, 2020), pp. 126-129, for a description of the unethical consent process employed in the "circumcise now/circumcise later" HIV research project conducted in Uganda.

54. https://www.youtube.com/watch?v=Cz8SD4niOVo.

55. https://qns.com/2013/11/queens-doctor-targeted-over-circumcisions/.

EPILOGUE

56. https://intactamerica.org/new-survey-finds-that-4-out-of-10-uncircumcised-boys-have-had-their-foreskins-forcibly-retracted-by-the-age-of-7/.

57. Seth Hemmelgarn, "Intactivist Jonathon Conte dead at 34," *Bay Area Reporter,* Wednesday May 18, 2016. https://www.ebar.com/story.php?246292.

58. Lesley Roberts, *A Is for Alex* (Cherish Editions: Newark, Nottinghamshire UK, 2020).

59. Cecile Richards, *Make Trouble: Standing Up, Speaking Out, and Finding the Courage to Lead* (New York: Touchstone, 2018), p. 164.